Communication Studies 20
Second Edition

Public Speaking,
San Jose State University

Department of Communication Studies

THOMSON
TM
CUSTOM PUBLISHING

Editor: Marc Bove
Publishing Services Supervisor: Donna Brown
Graphic Designer: Krista Pierson
Rights and Permissions Specialist: Kalina Ingham Hintz
Project Coordinator: Mary Snelling
Marketing Manager: Sara L. Hinckley

Thomson Custom Publishing
5191 Natorp Blvd.
Mason, Ohio 45040
USA

For information about our products, contact us:
1-800-355-9983
http://www.thomsoncustom.com

International Headquarters
Thomson Learning
International Division
290 Harbor Drive, 2nd Floor
Stamford, CT 06902-7477
USA

UK/Europe/Middle East/South Africa
Thomson Learning
Berkshire House
168-173 High Holborn
London WCIV 7AA

Asia
Thomson Learning
60 Albert Street, #15-01
Albert Complex
Singapore 189969

Canada
Nelson Thomson Learning
1120 Birchmount Road
Toronto, Ontario MIK 5G4
Canada
United Kingdom

Visit us at www.thomsoncustom.com and learn more about this book and other titles published by Thomson Learning Custom Publishing.

ISBN 0-759-33990-2

The Adaptable Courseware Program consists of products and additions to existing Custom Publishing products that are produced from camera-ready copy. Peer review, class testing, and accuracy are primarily the responsibility of the author(s).

For permission to use material from this text or product, submit a request online at
http://www.thomsonrights.com
Any additional questions about permissions can be submitted by email to thomsonrights@thomson.com

TABLE OF CONTENTS

For more information about Comm 20: Public Speaking at San Jos State University, contact:

Dr. Deanna L. Fassett, Department of Communication Studies
(408) 924-5511; dfassett@email.sjsu.edu

For more information about the Department of Communication Studies, contact:

Dr. Dennis Jaehne, Department Chair; (408) 924-5360

STUDENT INFORMATION SHEET

Name:
Social Security #:
Year in School:
Major:
E-mail Address:

Public speaking experience:

What helps you learn?

How comfortable are you speaking in front of a group?

How familiar are you with outlining?

How familiar are you with the SJSU library?

What are your areas of interest?

What topics might you be interested in speaking about in the future?

MULTICULTURAL GROUND RULES
for Public Speaking class

- Our primary commitment is to learn from the instructor, from each other, from materials and from our work. We acknowledge differences amongst us in skills, interests, values, scholarly orientations and experience.

- We acknowledge that racism, sexism, ageism, heterosexism, ableism, classism, anti-semitism, and other forms of discrimination exist and are likely to surface from time to time.

- We acknowledge that one of the meanings of racism is that we have been systematically taught misinformation about our own group and especially members of devalued groups and populations of color (this is true for both dominant and dominated group members). The same is true about other "isms" we are taught misinformation about ourselves and others regarding forms of difference and discrimination.

- We cannot be blamed for the misinformation we have heard but we will be held responsible for repeating misinformation after we have learned otherwise.

- Victims are not to be blamed for their oppression.

- We will assume that people are always doing the best they can, both to learn the material and to behave in non-racist, non-sexist, non-classist, non-heterosexist, and multiculturally productive ways.

- We will actively pursue opportunities to learn about our own groups and those of others, yet not enter or invade others' privacy when unwanted.

- We will share information about our groups with other students, and we will not demean, devalue, or "put down" people for their experiences or lifestyles.

- We each have an obligation to actively combat the myths and stereotypes about our own groups and other groups so that we can break down the walls that hinder group cooperation and group gain.

- We want to create a safe atmosphere for open discussion. Thus, at times, someone may wish to make a comment that s/he does not want repeated outside this class. If so, the person will preface the remarks with a request and we will agree to not repeat the remarks.

PUBLIC SPEAKING ETHICS

Research:

- Always be honest and truthful about your data and your interpretation of the data. Think through your interpretations very carefully and consider both sides.

- Always research multiple sides of an issue. You cannot ethically argue for one side or another without having a clear picture and a thorough understanding of what the other sides represent.

- Acknowledge counter arguments whenever it seems appropriate. Never mislead your audience by withholding vital information.

- Trust the audience members to ultimately know what is in their own best interest. Give them the most information you can, set up your arguments to the best of your ability, and then let them decide.

- Always, always, always, cite your sources in your outlines. Cite them in your speech whenever necessary. Otherwise, it is plagiarism.

Speaking:

- Choose a topic that is relevant to your audience and that you think has ethically sound goals.

- Think through the implications of your speech topic and who you are speaking to.

- Be fully prepared for your speech. KNOW your topic thoroughly.

- Do all you can to learn about your audience and then develop your speech for them.

- Never use fallacies or name calling.

- Utilize the public forum for quality discussion of important issues, not to slander.

- Be a model for quality public discussion that focuses on issues.

- Always be respectful of the titles and group designations by which people prefer to be identified.

Audience Member:

- Be open as a listener.

- Give the speaker enough time to present his/her point completely before you jump to conclusions.

- Address the speaker respectfully.

- Address the issues at hand, not the character of the speaker.

Ethical Dilemma 1

The Situation

You are giving a persuasive speech on the legalization of marijuana and you have found some excellent supporting materials (statistics and studies) in a pro-marijuana flyer you picked up at a downtown rally. The flyer is not professionally made and no sources for the information are listed, but the material is too good to ignore. You decide to go ahead and include the information in your speech even though you cannot validate its authenticity. What is the ethical quality of this situation?

Ethical Quality Scale

Highly Unethical	Moderately	Slightly	Neutral	Slightly	Moderately	Highly Ethical
1	2	3	4	5	6	7

Would your EQ rating vary depending on the following variables?

EQ: _____ The audience will never know.

EQ: _____ It is only a brief part of your argument.

EQ: _____ Your friend who is knowledgeable about the issue assures you the information is legitimate even though she cannot trace the source.

Ethical Dilemma 2

The Situation

You are scheduled to give a speech in COMM 20 tomorrow but, unfortunately, your recent chemistry final absorbed all of your energy, leaving you with little time to prepare your speech. Your helpful roommate saves the day and offers you her B+ speech from last semester. After contemplating your situation, you decide to deliver your roommate s speech. What is the ethical quality of this situation?

Ethical Quality Scale

Highly Unethical	Moderately	Slightly	Neutral	Slightly	Moderately	Highly Ethical
1	2	3	4	5	6	7

Would your EQ rating vary depending on the following variables?

EQ: _____ You changed the introduction and made minor adaptations through the body of the speech so it isn t copied word-for-word.

EQ: _____ You re typically a great student and clearly understand the principles of research and outlining so you probably would have done just as well, if not better, on your own if you had had the time.

EQ: _____ You are a graduating senior and can t afford to get anything less than a C in the class.

EQ: _____ You dislike the instructor.

Ethical Dilemma 3

The Situation

You are delivering a speech on wilderness safety and you wish to incorporate a great attention-getting story you heard about a man who had been chased up a tree by a moose in Montana. To add to the story s impact you decide to say that the situation actually happened to you, even though it didn t. What is the ethical quality of this situation?

Ethical Quality Scale

Highly Unethical	Moderately	Slightly	Neutral	Slightly	Moderately	Highly Ethical
1	2	3	4	5	6	7

Would your EQ rating vary depending on the following variables?

EQ: _____ No one will ever know.

EQ: _____ Something similar happened to you once.

EQ: _____ Your speech teacher emphasizes the importance of attention-getting strategies.

Ethical Dilemma 4

The Situation

The speech on abortion you will be delivering is in two days, but you have not had as much time to research this topic. The library is closed so it will be impossible for you to get secondary sources. You hear that a friend in your dorm has had an abortion, though, and you decide to interview her. Although your speech is supportive of the pro-life position, you tell your friend that you believe in a woman s right to choose. Basically, you tell your friend that you would like to know about the procedure and promise to keep her name confidential. While delivering your speech you violate this woman s privacy by divulging her name. What is the ethical quality of this situation?

Ethical Quality Scale

Highly Unethical	Moderately	Slightly	Neutral	Slightly	Moderately	Highly Ethical
1	2	3	4	5	6	7

Would your EQ rating vary depending on the following variables?

EQ: _____ Most of the students in your speech class live off campus and do not know this woman.

EQ: _____ You are a serious pro-life advocate and disrespect this woman for having had an abortion.

Ethical Dilemma 5

The Situation

When listening to an informative speech by one of your classmates, you realize that much of it is plagiarized from a magazine article you read a couple of weeks ago. After class you confront the student and tell him/her that you know what s/he has done. The student tries to convince you that it is no big deal and no one will know anyway because the article was not in a popular magazine. What is the ethical quality of this situation?

Ethical Quality Scale

Highly Unethical	Moderately	Slightly	Neutral	Slightly	Moderately	Highly Ethical
1	2	3	4	5	6	7

Would your EQ rating vary depending on the following variables?

EQ: _____ You dislike the student who is delivering the speech.

EQ: _____ The student is someone you have wanted to go out with all semester.

EQ: _____ At the beginning of the semester your teacher promised a monetary reward to anyone who reported the name(s) of any student(s) suspicious of plagiarism and/or cheating.

Ethical Dilemma 6

The Situation

In order to bolster your own credibility you try the following strategies. What is the Ethical Quality of each situation?

Ethical Quality Scale

Highly Unethical	Moderately	Slightly	Neutral	Slightly	Moderately	Highly Ethical
1	2	3	4	5	6	7

Would your EQ rating vary depending on the following variables?

EQ: _____ To establish competence you tell your audience that you have had an avid interest in your topic for the past year when in fact you have only studied it for the last month.

EQ: _____ Though you are typically a quiet and calm person, you intentionally act as though you have extremely high energy in order to appear dynamic.

EQ: _____ Your motives for speaking are really based on self interest, although you disguise them as concern for your audience s well being. For example, you try to convince your audience that earthquake insurance is essential. Mainly this is because you sell it and will profit from the business, yet you act as if the reason you really want them to buy it is so they will be protected in event of an earthquake.

Personal Report of Communication Apprehension 24

This instrument is composed of twenty-four statements concerning feelings about communicating with others. Please indicate the degree to which each statement applies to you by marking whether you:

Strongly Agree	Agree	Neutral	Disagree	Strongly Disagree
1	2	3	4	5

_____1. I dislike participating in group discussions.

_____2. Generally, I am comfortable while participating in group discussions.

_____3. I am tense and nervous while participating in group discussions.

_____4. I like to get involved in group discussions.

_____5. Engaging in a group discussion with new people makes me tense and nervous.

_____6. I am calm and relaxed while participating in group discussions.

_____7. Generally, I am nervous when I have to participate in a meeting.

_____8. Usually, I am comfortable when I have to participate in a meeting.

_____9. I am very calm and relaxed when I am called upon to express an opinion at a meeting.

_____10. I am afraid to express myself at meetings.

_____11. Communicating at meetings usually makes me uncomfortable.

_____12. I am very relaxed when answering questions at a meeting.

_____13. While participating in a conversation with a new acquaintance, I feel very nervous.

_____14. I have no fear of speaking up in conversations.

_____15. Ordinarily I am very tense and nervous in conversations.

_____16. Ordinarily I am very calm and relaxed in conversations.

_____17. While conversing with a new acquaintance, I feel very relaxed.

_____18. I'm afraid to speak up in conversations.

_____19. I have no fear of giving a speech.

_____20. Certain parts of my body feel very tense and rigid while giving a speech.

_____21. I feel relaxed while giving a speech.

_____22. My thoughts become confused and jumbled when I am giving a speech.

_____23. I face the prospect of giving a speech with confidence.

_____24. While giving a speech, I get so nervous I forget facts I really know.

SCORING:

Group discussion: 18 + (scores for items 2, 4, & 6) - (scores for items 1,3, & 5)

Meetings: 18 + (scores for items 8, 9, & 12) - (scores for items 7, 10, & 11)

Interpersonal: 18 + (scores for items 14, 16, & 17) - (scores for items 13, 15, & 18)

Public Speaking: 18 + (scores for items 19, 21, &23) - (scores for items 20, 22, &24)

Group Discussion Score: _____   Interpersonal Score: _____

Meetings Score: _____   Public Speaking Score: _____

To obtain your total score for the PRCA, simply add your sub scores together. _____

Scores can range from 24-120. Scores below 51 represent people who have very low CA. Scores between 51-80 represent people with average CA. Scores above 80 represent people who have high levels of trait CA.

NORMS FOR THE PRCA 24

	Mean	Standard Deviation	High	Low
For Total Score	65.6	15.3	> 80	< 51
Group:	15.4	4.8	> 20	< 11
Meeting:	16.4	4.2	> 20	< 13
Dyad (Interpersonal):	14.5	4.2	> 18	< 11
Public:	19.3	5.1	> 24	< 14

Source

McCroskey, J. C. (1982). *An introduction to rhetorical communication* (4th Ed). Englewood Cliffs, NJ: Prentice-Hall.

Personal Report of Public Speaking Anxiety (PRPSA)

Directions: Below are eighteen statements that people sometimes make about themselves. Please indicate whether or not you believe each statement applies to you by marking whether you:

Strongly Disagree	Disagree	Neutral	Agree	Strongly Agree
1	2	3	4	5

_____1. While preparing for giving a speech, I feel tense and nervous.

_____2. I feel tense when I see the words "speech" and "public speech" on a course outline when studying.

_____3. My thoughts become confused and jumbled when I am giving a speech.

_____4. Right after giving a speech I feel that I have had a pleasant experience.

_____5. I get anxious when I think about a speech coming up.

_____6. I have no fear of giving a speech.

_____7. Although I am nervous just before starting a speech, I soon settle down after starting and feel calm and comfortable.

_____8. I look forward to giving a speech.

_____9. When the instructor announces a speaking assignment in class, I can feel myself getting tense.

_____10. My hands tremble when I am giving a speech.

_____11. I feel relaxed while giving a speech.

_____12. I enjoy preparing for a speech.

_____13. I am in constant fear of forgetting what I prepared to say.

_____14. I get anxious if someone asks me something about my topic that I don't know.

_____15. I face the prospect of giving a speech with confidence.

_____16. I feel that I am in complete possession of myself while giving a speech.

_____17. My mind is clear when giving a speech.

_____18. I do not dread giving a speech.

_____19. I perspire just before starting a speech.

_____20. My heart beats very fast just as I start a speech.

_____21. I experience considerable anxiety while sitting in the room just before my speech starts.

_____22. Certain parts of my body feel very tense and rigid while giving a speech.

_____23. Realizing that only a little time remains in a speech makes me very tense and anxious.

_____24. While giving a speech, I know I can control my feelings of tension and stress.

_____25. I breathe faster just before starting a speech.

_____26. I feel comfortable and relaxed in the hour or so just before giving a speech.

_____27. I do poorer on speeches because I am anxious.

_____28. I feel anxious when the teacher announces the date of a speaking assignment.

_____29. When I make a mistake while giving a speech, I find it hard to concentrate on the parts that follow.

_____30. During an important speech I experience a feeling of helplessness building up inside me.

_____31. I have trouble falling asleep the night before a speech.

_____32. My heart beats very fast while I present a speech.

_____33. I feel anxious while waiting to give my speech.

_____34. While giving a speech, I get so nervous I forget facts I really know.

Scoring: To determine your score on the PRPSA, complete the following steps:

Step 1. Add scores for items 1, 2, 3, 5, 9, 10, 13, 14, 19, 20, 21, 22, 23, 25, 27, 28, 29, 30, 31, 32, 33, and 34

Step 2. Add the scores for items 4, 6, 7, 8, 11, 12, 15, 16, 17, 18, 24, and 26

Step 3. Complete the following formula:

$$PRPSA = 1322 - \text{Total from Step 1} + \text{Total from Step 2}$$

Your score should be between 34 and 170. If your score is below 34 or above 170, you have made a mistake in computing the score.

High => 131   Low = < 98   Moderate 98-131

Mean = 114.6   SD = 17.2

Source:

McCroskey, J. C. (1970). Measures of communication-bound anxiety. *Speech Monographs, 37*, 269-277.

WHY CITE SOURCES?

The American Heritage Dictionary defines plagiarism as stealing and using "ideas and writings of another as one's own." The principal reason for citing sources is:

To Protect   We protect ourselves from committing plagiarism by ensuring that our information is reliable and is accurately presented.

To Acknowledge   We want to give credit where credit is due.

To Support   We want a speech with reliable facts, forcing a potentially unfavorable audience member to argue with facts rather than with opinions.

To Serve   We help the audience locate additional information about the subject.

**To Make
the Grade**   We want to get the best grade possible for our efforts; a well organized and well-documented speech is more likely to receive a better grade than one that is not.

TYPES OF SOURCES

Primary sources are those sources that gathered or first reported the information.

Secondary sources use information from primary sources.

For example, each year the Department of Labor compiles statistics about unemployment rates. If the statistics you found about unemployment came directly from the Dept. of Labor reports, your evidence would be from a **primary** source; if your statistics came from a *Time* magazine article about unemployment, you would be using a **secondary** source.

Whenever possible, rely on primary sources for your information, especially for your main points. When you use secondary sources, you may be getting only part of the information and you cannot always be sure that the information has been reported accurately.

USING SOURCE CITATIONS

I. There are instances when citing a source is required for the speeches in this class.

    A. When quoting directly from a source, a citation is required.

        1. A direct quote is copied word-for-word as the original.

        2. A direct quote can be either spoken or written.

    B. When quoting indirectly from a source, a citation is required.

        1. An indirect quote is taking an idea or information and putting it into your own words.

        2. An indirect quote can be written or spoken.

    C. When using statistical information, a citation is required.

        1. Statistics can be reported in the form of percentages.

        2. Statistics can be reported in the form of ratio.

        3. Statistics can be reported in the form of straight numbers.

        (Consult The Speaker s Handbook for cautions about correctly using statistics.)

II. There are particular ways to cite a source.

    A. Citations in your speech should include thorough but pertinent information.

        1. The author(s) or sponsoring agency of the source.

            a. Pick sources that are reasonably well-known to your audience, if possible.

            b. Establish the credibility of the author if not well known.

                1) Testimony

                2) Experience

                3) Publication

        2. The date of the source.

            a. When citing books or agency reports, the year is usually adequate.

            b. Newspapers and magazines should include the full date.

    B. **All** sources that are cited in your speech/outline should be included in reference list.

    C. Cite the source every time you use it, both in your speech and on the outline.

        1. Err on the side of over-citing rather than under-citing.

        2. It is better to be redundant than to have the audience wonder where you obtained your information.

A.P.A. Citation Format

References
(Always double-space citations and put References (centered) at the top of the listing.)

Citing a book:

Sprague, J., & Stuart, D. (1995). *The speaker s handbook* (6th ed.). Belmont, CA: Wadsworth.

Citing an article in a book:

Anderson, P.A. (1985). Nonverbal immediacy in interpersonal communication. In A. W. Sigman &

   S. Feldstein (Eds.), *Multicultural integrations of nonverbal behavior* (pp. 1-36). Hillside, NJ:

   Lawrence Erlbaum Associates.

Citing when there is no author or editor:

College bound seniors. (1979). Princeton, NJ: College Board Publications.

Citing a journal article:

Cooper, M. (1988). Rhetorical criticism and Foucault s philosophy of discursive events. *Central States*

   Speech Journal, 39, 1-17.

Citing a magazine article:

Gardner, H. (1981, December). Do babies sing a universal song? *Psychology Today*, 70-76.

Citing a newspaper article:

Duke, J. (1981, September 4). Basketball player loses position. *San Diego Tribune*, p. 7.

Citing a brochure:

Institute for Teaching and Learning (1993). *Guidelines for teaching communicatively apprehensive students*

   (3rd Ed.) [Brochure]. Lexington, KY: Author.

Citing an interview:

Dussik, D.P. (1989, January 3). Instructor at San Jose State University. (408) 924-5590.

Citing from a database:

Levin, G. (1997, December 15). TV: Back to the future. *Variety, 369*, 1-3. Retrieved: August 8, 2001,

   from Expanded Academic ASAP database (A20385512).

You may find other citations that are not listed here in Publication Manual of the American Psychological Association, 5th ed., 2001. This is located at the Reference Desk in the library.

USING THE INTERNET IN SPEECHES

The World Wide Web is full of information, but not all sources are equally valuable or reliable. Unlike scholarly journals, books or news magazines, which are reviewed by editors or experts in the fields before being published, anyone can post on the internet; they are rarely held accountable for what is posted. Therefore, you are encouraged to use the Web for initial research or supplemental information, but use sources that are more reliable and verifiable (e.g. a recent book) for important points in your speech.

There are issues to consider when evaluating any source. When using the internet, these become crucial.

Content

- What is the purpose of the text (web page)?
- How comprehensive is the information?
- What other resources are available in the particular area?
- Who is the intended audience?

Source and Date

- Who is the author or producer?
- What is the expertise of the author of the text and/or the creator of the web page?
- Is any sort of bias evident?
- When was the item produced? When was it posted? When was it last revised?
- How up-to-date are the links?
- Is contact information for the author included in the document?

Structure

- Do the graphics (visual aids) serve a function, or are they decorative?
- Does the text follow basic rules of grammar, spelling, and composition?
- Are links provided to web subject trees or lists of subject-arranged web sources?

Citing

Since the purpose of citing sources is to allow others to find the same information, it is crucial that you cite Internet sources as completely as possible. Cite the author s last name and first initial, then the date on which the page was created or updated, or if that is unknown the date of the search. The title should be in italics or underlined followed by Accessed on and the date you last looked at the website. Then include the URL http/path. For example:

Guidan, J. (1995, October). *Critical considerations of the internet.* Accessed on March 12, 1997 at http://www.ucla.edu/campus/computing/bruinonline/trainers/critical.html

PERSONAL INVENTORY OF TOPICS AND IDEAS

Places	People

Events	Organizations

Hobbies	TV Programs

Books	Personal Goals

Professional Goals	Beliefs

Social Issues	Public Policies

From Sellnow, D. (2002). Public speaking: A process approach. Orlando, FL: Harcourt College Publishers.

NARROWING SPEECH TOPICS

SUBJECT		SPEECH TOPIC

(1)   Narrow the subject in time

      Pesticides   ----------➤   The current controversy over the urban spraying for medflies in Southern California

      Music   ----------➤   The origins of jazz

      Drug Use   ----------➤   The current medical information on the consequences of using crack cocaine

(2)   Narrow the subject in space

      Deforestation   ----------➤   The deforestation of the Brazilian rain forest

(3)   Narrow the subject to a subproblem

      Energy conservation   ----------➤   The economics of solar energy

(4)   Discuss a portion of a process

      Administration of justice   ----------➤   The differences between a court martial and a civilian trial

An example of a single topic narrowed by all four methods:

General subject:	International diplomacy
Narrowed in space:	Central America
Narrowed to a subproblem:	Nicaraguan presidential election
Narrowed in time:	February 1989
Narrowed to a portion of a process:	The role of foreign monitors to oversee elections

TOPIC SELECTION & ANALYSIS WORKSHEET

1. Write down four topics that interest you or that you are knowledgeable about.

   A)

   B)

   C)

   D)

Pick two of the four topics and narrow them down (by being more specific in terms of the focus)

   A)

   B)

For each of the two narrowed topics decide what specific purpose would be best for the topic. (Keep in mind, Speech 1 is a demonstration speech and Speech 2 is an informative speech.)

   A)

   B)

Consider some possible main points for these topics. Write two sample thesis statements for each topic. (Remember: your thesis statements should be single declarative sentences that capture the central idea of your topic and unify its main points.)

   A1)

   A2)

   B1)

   B2)

5. On a separate sheet of paper, **TYPE** the following information: **a)** the topic you will focus on for Speech 2 **b)** the specific purpose of your speech and **c)** a possible thesis statement.

OUTLINE WORKSHEET

TOPIC:

ORGANIZATIONAL PATTERN:

SPECIFIC PURPOSE:

PRIMARY AUDIENCE OUTCOME:

THESIS STATEMENT (state central idea, the essence of the speech):

INTRODUCTION

ATTENTION GETTER:

PSYCHOLOGICAL ORIENTATION (relate topic to this audience):

LOGICAL ORIENTATION (state thesis, then preview main points):

BODY

•2-5 MAIN POINTS PREFERRED •USE ONLY COMPLETE SENTENCES

I. MAIN POINT (state as a single declarative sentence):

    A. SUBPOINT:

        1.
           a.
           b.
        2.
           a.
           b.

    B. SUBPOINT:

1.
    a.
    b.
2.
    a.
    b.

C.   SUBPOINT:

1.
    a.
    b.
2.
    a.
    b.

Transition:

II.   MAIN POINT (state as a single declarative sentence):

A.   SUBPOINT:

1.
    a.
    b.
2.
    a.
    b.

B.   SUBPOINT:

1.
    a.
    b.
2.
    a.
    b.

C.   SUBPOINT:

1.
    a.
    b.
2.
    a.

                    b.

Transition:

III.   MAIN POINT (state as a single declarative sentence):

    A.   SUBPOINT:

        1.
                a.
                b.
        2.
                a.
                b.

    B.   SUBPOINT:

        1.
                a.
                b.
        2.
                a.
                b.

    C.   SUBPOINT:

        1.
                a.
                b.
        2.
                a.
                b.

CONCLUSION

LOGICAL CLOSURE (restate main points and thesis):

PSYCHOLOGICAL CLOSURE (relate importance and relevance to this audience):

CLINCHER (end with a bang, not a whimper):

CREATING NOTE CARDS

1. Purchase 4x 6 note cards because they are easy to hold, and do not hinder gestures.

2. Write legibly; the printing or writing on your note card should be clear and easy to read.

3. Number your cards in the upper right hand corner, so that you can put them in place quickly if they get out of order.

4. Plan on two to four card for each five minutes you plan to talk.

5. Try to use no more than six or seven lines per card, and space your lines so that you can find your place instantly.

6. Write on only one side of each card, because turning cards over can be distracting.

7. Keep in mind that you are preparing notes, not a manuscript. Note cards are to be referred to not read from. Write down only what you find you need during practice: only key words and short phrases.

8. Completely write out any long quotations, expert testimony, and statistics you plan to use in your talk that you are not able to memorize.

9. There should be lots of visual cues — highlight important ideas and circle or underline words you want to emphasize during delivery.

10. Put words such as pause or slow down on your cards to serve as delivery reminders.

11. Practice in front of a mirror using your note cards. You should be able to look down, see what is next, and then talk about it. Revise them if they are not as helpful as you would like.

12. When you actually give your speech, do not try to hide your note cards from your audience. However, never wave them around. When you read a direct quotation or give complicated statistics, hold up a card and look at it frequently to show your audience that you are being as accurate as possible.

NOTECARD EXAMPLES

PROTOCOL FOR SPEECH DAYS

SPEAKERS:

1. Get to class on time preferably a few minutes early.
2. Turn in your outline and evaluation form to the instructor <u>before</u> speeches begin.
3. When appropriate, be sure your videotape is advanced to the end of your most recent speech and that your name is on both the tape and the box. Give the tape to the video operator before speeches begin.
4. Be as organized as possible before class begins. Have your visual aids and equipment ready in order to minimize set-up time between speeches.
5. Try to treat this entire period as a real audience setting. Let s make this as close to a formal public event as possible. Talk to me about requirements and assignments before or after class. Do not break the mood of a speaking situation with questions, conferences, apologies, etc.

AUDIENCE:

1. Be there on time. If you are unavoidably late, wait outside the door and enter between speeches.
2. You are required to be courteous; but beyond that, you are requested to be attentive, responsive, supportive listeners.
3. When requested, you should provide feedback. Try not to write during the speech, but rather during the question/answer periods after the speech. Finish responses at the end of class if you need a few more minutes. Try to write <u>specific, constructive, and tactful</u> comments.
4. Ask penetrating but not hostile questions. This will make the class more interesting for all of us (and it contributes to your participation grade).

VIDEO OPERATOR:

1. Arrive five minutes early and review the working of the equipment.
2. Collect the videotapes form the speakers and arrange them in order.
3. Insert each tape, adjust the camera to the speaker s height, focus and give the speaker a nod to begin.
4. During the speech leave the camera at a nearly full figure shot. Try to follow the speaker s movement and include visual aids and demonstrations, but do not make constant adjustments.
5. Tape the question and answer period, as well as the speech.
6. Return the tapes to the speakers at the end of class.
7. Thank you for volunteering.

SPEECH #1
DEMONSTRATION

PURPOSE OF ASSIGNMENT:

The primary purpose of demonstration speaking is to help clarify a complex process, idea or event for your audience. In other words, in this approximately 5 minute speech, you are to demonstrate (or teach us) how to do something; what you choose to demonstrate can be as simple or as complicated as you like, so long as it has something to do with your culture. You are welcome to define culture broadly i.e., in addition to your racial background or ethnic heritage, you might also consider your gender, sexuality, age, or other co-cultural affiliations (e.g., musician, skater, cheerleader, and so on). Keep in mind that effective use of visual aids will likely help your audience better understand and learn what you choose to demonstrate.

Please explore your creative options (within the guidelines of common sense and university policy). Refer to the text as you see fit. Your grade will be based on the following:

REQUIREMENTS:

- ◆ Your topic should be informative and challenging to this audience.
- ◆ The speech should be **approximately 5 minutes**.
- ◆ Delivery is to be extemporaneous. Use up to four notecards. These are to be turned in following your speech upon your instructor s request.
- ◆ The introduction and conclusion should be fully developed.
- ◆ There should be a definite, logical transition bridging each component of the speech.
- ◆ Each main point should be clearly stated and developed.
- ◆ Use at least **one visual aid** according to the guidelines presented in the text.
- ◆ Adhere to the principles of clear explanation. Use organizers (signposts, enumeration, acronyms, slogans), emphasis cues, and figurative analogies. Also use definitions where appropriate.
- ◆ Be prepared to answer questions from the audience after the conclusion of your speech.
- ◆ A **typed, full-sentence** outline (following the correct format) is required and should be submitted on the day of your speech. The following elements are to be included and **labeled in the margin or where appropriate:**
  - ▪ Organizational pattern
  - ▪ Specific purpose & primary audience outcome
  - ▪ Thesis statement
  - ▪ Three functions of your introduction and conclusion
  - ▪ Transitions between main points
  - ▪ A reference list in APA format
- ◆ Your presentation skills should include:
  - ▪ Natural and conversational delivery
  - ▪ Appropriate oral style
  - ▪ **Extemporaneous mode** using speech notes (notecards or key word outline)
  - ▪ Effective vocal and physical delivery skills
  - ▪ Effective use of visual aids

♦ **Bring video tape** the day of your speech per your instructor s request.

CRITERIA FOR EVALUATION:

To receive a passing grade for this assignment you need to make an earnest attempt at meeting the above requirements. In other words, if there are no serious deviations from the above requirements, expect to receive about 70% of the possible points (C range). If you not only meet the minimal requirements, but carry them out well, expect to receive 80-89% (B range) or, if you carry them out exceptionally well, expect to receive 90-100% (A range) of the possible points. Total points for the assignment will be weighted as follows:

Introduction	25 points
Organization	25 points
Development	25 points
Conclusion	25 points
Delivery	25 points
Total	**125 points**
(Outline:	25 points)

SUGGESTIONS FOR PREPARATION:

Keep in mind the importance of clarity. This is largely achieved through effective organization. Confine your speech to two or three main ideas and group the other points under these. Clarify the relationship between your points. Use clear, explicit previews, transitions, and summaries. Keep your speech moving ahead according to a well developed plan; do not jump back and forth from one idea to another.

Prepare your visual aids and gather your props and materials at once and **practice** with them.

Time your speech when practicing. After you have written your outline, set it aside and practice speaking **from brief notes** on notecards.

Practice your speech several times, but **do not memorize it.**

On the day of the speech bring the following:

➢ Video tape per your instructor s request
➢ Your typed, full-sentence outline
➢ Notecards
➢ Evaluation Form
➢ Visual Aid

Speech 1: Demonstration Speech

Introduction: _____ Strengths: _____ ?s/suggestions/not-so-strengths _____

Attention-getting Material
_____ out of 5 pts possible

Thematic statement
_____ out of 10 pts possible

Preview
_____ out of 5 pts possible

Establishing credibility
_____ out of 5 pts possible

Organization: _____ Strengths: _____ ?s/suggestions/not-so-strengths _____

Logical organization
_____ out of 25 pts possible

Development _____ Strengths: _____ ?s/suggestions/not-so-strengths _____

Appropriate development
_____ out of 25 pts possible

Conclusion: _____ Strengths: _____ ?s/suggestions/not-so-strengths _____

Summary/Review
_____ out of 10 pts possible

Closure
_____ out of 15 pts possible

Delivery: _____ Strengths: _____ ?s/suggestions/not-so-strengths: _____

Effective extemporaneous delivery
_____ out of 25 pts possible

Total: _____ out of 125 points possible; Grade: _____

Outline: _____ out of 25 points possible
Peer Feedback: _____ out of 20 points possible

Peer Feedback Form

Speaker: _____   Respondent: _____

1=missing   2=average   3=good   4=excellent

<u>Introduction:</u>

Attention-getter effectiveness   1   2   3   4

Thesis   1   2   3   4

    What was the thesis? _____

Establishing credibility   1   2   3   4

<u>Body:</u>

    What were the main points?: _____
_____
_____
_____
_____
_____

Organized Effectively   1   2   3   4

Sufficient Development   1   2   3   4

Effective Use of Transitions?   1   2   3   4

<u>Conclusion:</u>

Summary/Review   1   2   3   4

Closure   1   2   3   4

    Were you left with a lasting impression? What was it?:

    Write at least one question to ask the speaker when s/he has concluded:

    Note at least two strengths of this presentation:

    Note one or two areas for improvement:

SELF-EVALUATION GUIDELINES

Spend some time reflecting on the videotape of your demonstration speech (and then later, in your second self-evaluation, on your experiences with the second speech in comparison with this first speech), and then write a 2-3 page paper (typed, double-spaced, 10 or 12 point font) evaluation of your presentation. What were the specific strengths you believe you demonstrated? What were specific areas of weakness that you believe diminished the effectiveness of the presentation? Remember, it is NOT sufficient to focus your evaluation entirely on the negatives or solely on delivery. If you get stuck, you might find it useful to consider the following questions:

* preparation what did you do to prepare for this speech? What m ight you have done (or will you try to do for the next speech) differently in order for a more effective speech?

* introduction how effective was your attention-getting strategy? How effective were you at establishing credibility?

* body/content although you were familiar with the content of your speech, your audience was only exposed to it for five to eight minutes or so. Were you clear in your theme? How would you revise your speech so that you could improve it? What can you say about the organization of your speech? Were your ideas developed thoroughly? You might even consider looking at your strongest (or your weakest) transition and stating why you think it was effective (or ineffective).

* conclusion did you clearly summarize key points from your speech? Did you leave your audience with a lasting impression?

* delivery what were your strengths? What do you need to improve?

20 points possible

SUPPORTING MATERIALS

1. DEFINITIONS

Logical - Denotative meaning

Angioplasty is a medical procedure used to clear blocked arteries.

Etymological or Historical - How the word was derived.

Angio is derived from Greek and refers to a blood vessel.
Plasty refers to molding or surgery.
Therefore, angioplasty can be loosely understood as blood vessel surgery.

Operational - How the concept or object works or operates.

Angioplasty involves inserting a small deflated balloon into the artery and inflating the balloon, thus pressing plaque to the walls of the artery and allowing for the free flow of blood.

Negation - explains what something is not.

Although angioplasty is a surgical procedure, it is not the same type of surgery as a heart bypass procedure.

Authority - the definition accepted by an authority.

The American Medical Association classifies angioplasty as a surgical procedure.

Example - point at it verbally or literally.

Angioplasty means inserting a balloon into the artery, like this [show a visual aid illustrating deflated or inflated balloon in an artery].

2. EXAMPLES

Illustrate (factual): The San Andreas Fault is an example of a strike-slip fault.

Clarify (hypothetical): What would the Clinton Health Care Plan accomplish? Imagine you got sick but couldn t take it easy because you have so much schoolwork to do. You get worse and wind up in the hospital. The hospital is scary enough, but you re even more concerned because you don t have insurance. Who is going to pay for this? Under the Clinton Plan, you wouldn t have to worry about anything because you would be covered.

3. STATISTICS

• Thirty-seven million Americans don t have health insurance.

• One in four women will be raped in their lifetime.

• More people are killed in drunk driving accidents every year than were killed in the entire Vietnam War.

4. TESTIMONY

Opinion - Former Surgeon General C. Everett Koop supports the Clinton Health Care Plan.

Experience - Mark Jackson has worked as an animal behaviorist for 20 years and says zoo animals do not suffer as a result of captivity.

INFORMATIVE STRATEGIES

➤ Avoid information overload.

➤ Give your audience a road map.

➤ Move from the simple to the complex.

➤ Move from the familiar to the unfamiliar.

➤ Use organizers:

  ▪ Signposts *so by reducing, recycling, and reusing, you can limit the amount of waste going to your local landfill.*

  ▪ Enumeration *Three steps you can take to tackle solid waste are first,   recycle, second, reduce, and third, reuse.*

  ▪ Slogans *So when trash day comes, remember the three R s: recycle, reduce, and reuse.*

  ▪ Acronyms see the text

➤ Use emphasis cues:

  ▪ *If you ve gained anything here today, I hope it s a realization. A realization that this isn t your problem, it isn t my problem; it s <u>our</u> problem.*

➤ Use examples:

  ▪ Examples make claims or abstract information concrete.

➤ Use analogies:

  ▪ Move from the known to the unknown

  ▪ *Just as your car needs gas to run, your body needs calories.*

➤ Use multiple channels--visual, auditory, and kinesthetic

➤ Use repetition

  ▪ If an idea is important, repeat it, reinforce it, and tie back to it.

ATTENTION FACTORS

Once you gain your audience s attention (via the introduction), you need to hold their attention throughout your speech. You can capture and hold the audience s attention in a variety of ways. *The Speaker s Handbook* presents nine ways in which you can tailor your ideas. Can you identify the following attention factors?

1. Take John over there. Imagine what he d look like with his hair styled and with a three-piece suit, a Brooks Brothers shirt, a silk tie, and a black leather briefcase.

2. Do you realize how much fast food is consumed by our student body? Within four blocks of this classroom are nine restaurants, including a McDonald s, Jack-in-the-Box, Taco Bell, and a Burger King. Even the Student Union runs a fast food counter.

3. The London postal or zip codes are similar to directions on a compass. The initial letters of the codes indicate directions, and the next set of numbers represent degrees of longitude or latitude.

4. A home that costs three million dollars and a breakfast that costs five thousand are disquieting facts to the millions who live in a hut and dine on a crust. The fact that a man has an income of twenty million dollars falls strangely on the ears of those who hear it, as they sit empty-handed with children crying for bread.

5. [You begin a speech on retardation with the scenario of a developmentally disabled child; then, after describing the causes of retardation and care for the retarded, you reveal that you had been talking about your brother.]

6. Students who take an internship while in college, find jobs after graduation three times as fast as those who don t.

7. A friend of mine had a crush on one of the prettiest women in the freshman class. He was in two courses with her but could never find the right moment to introduce himself. One day in the cafeteria he ended up standing in line right behind her. Because he felt so self-conscious, his voice froze, and as they moved along the serving counter, he felt yet another opportunity slipping away. Suddenly, the girl turned to him and pointed at a selection. Do you know what this is? she asked. Y-yes, he replied, that s Don MacKensie. Hi, I m macaroni salad.

8. Judith Penley paid the price of a clean conscience with her life. Immediately after taking part in an outside investigation of her employer . . . several attempts were made on her life. Scared and confused, Judith told investigators she knew of no one who would ever want to hurt her. The next day, Judith was brutally gunned down as she waited for a friend. With echoes of Karen Silkwood, Newsweek reports that investigators drew an obvious connection.

9. The roaring river of innovation has overflowed its banks, flooding our environment with change. Humans are swimming in a sea of technology.

LIVELY LANGUAGE WORKSHEET

For each of the following common words, substitute a more uncommon word or phrase - something that is more concrete, animated, or intense. Then use the word or phrase in a sentence, preferably a sentence that relates to your speech topic, if appropriate.

Solution:

Tired:

Wrong:

Problem:

Money:

End:

Decrease:

Caring:

Lazy:

Angry:

Cheap:

Change:

SPEECH #2
INFORMATIVE

PURPOSE OF ASSIGNMENT:

The primary purpose of informative speaking is to ensure the audience's clear understanding of the ideas presented. The purpose of Speech #1 is to present a **clear explanation of complex material** to the audience. In other words, your task is to explain something that requires a human to explain it. Your topic should be intellectually challenging, informative and interesting to your audience. You are required to do research and cite your sources. You should use various supporting materials, visual aids, and attention factors to make the speech clear and interesting to the audience.

REQUIREMENTS:

- Your topic should be informative and challenging to this audience.
- The speech should be **approximately five minutes**.
- Delivery is to be extemporaneous. Use up to four notecards. These are to be turned in following your speech upon your instructor s request.
- The introduction and conclusion should be fully developed that is, they should include the three clearly identifiable parts.
- There should be a definite, logical transition bridging each component of the speech.
- Each main point should be clearly stated and developed.
- Use at least **three different types of supporting materials**.
- Use at least **three different types of attention factors**.
- Use at least **one visual aid** according to the guidelines presented in the text.
- Adhere to the principles of clear explanation. Use organizers (signposts, enumeration, acronyms, slogans), emphasis cues, and figurative analogies. Also use definitions where appropriate.
- Be prepared to answer questions from the audience after the conclusion of your speech.
- A **typed, full-sentence** outline (following the correct format) is required and should be submitted on the day of your speech. The following elements are to be included and **labeled in the margin or where appropriate** (see sample outlines for example):
  - Organizational pattern
  - Specific purpose & primary audience outcome
  - Thesis statement
  - Three functions of your introduction and conclusion
  - Transitions between main points
  - At least three different types of supporting materials (i.e. examples, testimony, statistics, explanation, definition)
  - At least three different types of attention factors (i.e. suspense, proximity, the Vital, humor, familiarity, movement, reality, novelty)
  - Four source citations in the text of the outline
  - A reference list in APA format with **at least four different source citations**
- Your presentation skills should include:
  - Natural and conversational delivery

- ▪ Appropriate oral style
- ▪ **Extemporaneous mode** using speech notes (notecards)
- ▪ Effective vocal and physical delivery skills
- ▪ Effective use of visual aids
- ♦ **Bring video tape** the day of your speech per your instructor s request.

CRITERIA FOR EVALUATION:

To receive a passing grade for this assignment you need to make an earnest attempt at meeting the above requirements. In other words, if there are no serious deviations from the above requirements, expect to receive about 70% of the possible points (C range). If you not only meet the minimal requirements, but carry them out well, expect to receive 80-89% (B range) or, if you carry them out exceptionally well, expect to receive 90-100% (A range) of the possible points. Total points for the assignment will be weighted as follows:

Introduction	15 points
Organization	50 points
Development	50 points
Conclusion	15 points
Delivery	20 points
Total	**150 points**
(Outline:	50 points possible)

SUGGESTIONS FOR PREPARATION:

Keep in mind the importance of clarity. This is largely achieved through effective organization. Confine your speech to two or three main ideas and group the other points under these. Clarify the relationship between your points. Use clear, explicit previews, transitions, and summaries. Keep your speech moving ahead according to a well developed plan; do not jump back and forth from one idea to another. A good place to look for topic ideas is in local newspapers, including the campus newspaper the *Spartan Daily*. (Hint: The editorial and commentary pages are good resources for controversial and timely issues.)

Prepare your visual aids and gather your props and materials at once and **practice** with them. Time your speech when practicing. After you have written your outline, set it aside and practice speaking **from brief notes** on notecards. Practice your speech several times, but **do not memorize it.**

On the day of the speech bring the following:

- ➢ Video tape per your instructor s request
- ➢ Your typed, full-sentence outline
- ➢ Notecards
- ➢ Evaluation Form
- ➢ Visual Aid

OUTLINE WORKSHEET

TOPIC:

ORGANIZATIONAL PATTERN:

SPECIFIC PURPOSE:

PRIMARY AUDIENCE OUTCOME:

THESIS STATEMENT (state central idea, the essence of the speech):

INTRODUCTION

ATTENTION GETTER:

PSYCHOLOGICAL ORIENTATION (relate topic to this audience):

LOGICAL ORIENTATION (state thesis, then preview main points):

BODY

•2-5 MAIN POINTS PREFERRED •USE ONLY COMPLETE SENTENCES

I.   MAIN POINT (state as a single declarative sentence):

    A.   SUBPOINT:

        1.
           a.
           b.
        2.
           a.
           b.

    B.   SUBPOINT:

1.
    a.
    b.
2.
    a.
    b.

C.   SUBPOINT:

   1.
      a.
      b.
   2.
      a.
      b.

Transition:

II.   MAIN POINT (state as a single declarative sentence):

   A.   SUBPOINT:

     1.
       a.
       b.
     2.
       a.
       b.

   B.   SUBPOINT:

     1.
       a.
       b.
     2.
       a.
       b.

   C.   SUBPOINT:

     1.
       a.
       b.
     2.
       a.

b.

Transition:

III.   MAIN POINT (state as a single declarative sentence):

     A.   SUBPOINT:

          1.
             a.
             b.
          2.
             a.
             b.

     B.   SUBPOINT:

          1.
             a.
             b.
          2.
             a.
             b.

     C.   SUBPOINT:

          1.
             a.
             b.
          2.
             a.
             b.

CONCLUSION

LOGICAL CLOSURE (restate main points and thesis):

PSYCHOLOGICAL CLOSURE (relate importance and relevance to this audience):

CLINCHER (end with a bang, not a whimper):

Speech 2: Informative

Introduction: _____ Strengths: _____ ?s/suggestions/not-so-strengths ____

Attention-getting Material
_____ out of 5 pts possible

Thematic statement/Preview
_____ out of 5 pts possible

Establishing credibility
_____ out of 5 pts possible

Organization: _____ Strengths: _____ ?s/suggestions/not-so-strengths ____

Logical organization
_____ out of 50 pts possible

Development _____ Strengths: _____ ?s/suggestions/not-so-strengths ____

Appropriate development
_____ out of 50 pts possible

Conclusion: _____ Strengths: _____ ?s/suggestions/not-so-strengths ____

Summary/Review
_____ out of 5 pts possible

Closure
_____ out of 10 pts possible

Delivery: _____ Strengths: _____ ?s/suggestions/not-so-strengths: ____

Effective extemporaneous delivery
_____ out of 20 pts possible

Total: _____ out of 150 points possible; Grade: _____

Outline: _____ out of 50 points possible
Peer Feedback: _____ out of 20 points possible

Peer Feedback Form

Speaker: _____   Respondent: _____

1=missing   2=average   3=good   4=excellent

Introduction:

Attention-getter effectiveness   1   2   3   4

Thesis   1   2   3   4

   What was the thesis? _____

Establishing credibility   1   2   3   4

Body:

   What were the main points?: _____
   _____
   _____
   _____
   _____

Organized Effectively   1   2   3   4

Sufficient Development   1   2   3   4

Effective Use of Transitions?   1   2   3   4

Conclusion:

Summary/Review   1   2   3   4

Closure   1   2   3   4

   Were you left with a lasting impression? What was it?:

   Write at least one question to ask the speaker when s/he has concluded:

   Note at least two strengths of this presentation:

   Note one or two areas for improvement:

REASONING GUIDELINES

(1) Make your reasoning clear to your listeners. It is not enough to simply present the evidence (supporting materials). Tell the audience how you reached your conclusions. The audience may come to very different conclusions so you must tell them how and why you arrived at the conclusions that you did.

(2) Organize your points to show logical relationships. Although your conclusions may be found at all levels of your speech (as your thesis sentence, main points or subpoints), you must lay out your claims and explain your reasoning logically. (Don t forget to use organizers and emphasis cues where they will be helpful).

(3) Use transitions (internal summaries and previews) to demonstrate your reasoning. Do not forget to write your transitions into your outline. This will help you to be clear about your reasoning, and it will show me that you have carefully thought out the connections between ideas. It will also help your audience to understand your perspective and why you came to the conclusions that you did. DO NOT ASSUME THAT YOUR AUDIENCE WILL ARRIVE AT THE SAME CONCLUSIONS THAT YOU DID. SPELL IT OUT!

(4) Use appropriate language with different forms of reasoning.

    (a) Show the strength of your examples when using <u>induction</u>:

        One case that supports my claim is . . .

        These statistics illustrate a widespread . . .

        Another example that adds to this pattern is . . .

        Although not true in every case, I have demonstrated that the importance of this pattern cannot be overlooked.

        I can say with near certainty . . .

        Evidence strongly indicates . . .

(b) State your premises and spell out your reasoning when using <u>deduction</u>:

Underlying my position is one of the fundamental tenets of our

constitution . . .

My argument rests on the assumption that . . .

I hope you will agree that . . .

Since I ve shown you X and Y, I m sure you ll see how I reached my conclusion . . .

Therefore . . .

These statistics mean . . .

(c) Qualify your causal claims by demonstrating the strength of the

<u>causal relationship.</u> (Answer the questions that qualify the strength of causality).

There may be many causes, but the one I have identified is a major

cause . . .

In the vast majority of cases, X has been shown to cause Y.

In every case I have shown you, when taxes went down, the economy improved.

For every unit of increase in X, there was a proportionate increase in Y.

Although not all criminals are victims of child abuse, I have demonstrated that it is one

of the major contributing factors.

(d) <u>To reason by analogy</u>, show the points of similarity and explain any points of

difference that may be important to your audience or case.

I have shown you how Sunnyvale and San Jose are alike in many important ways that

will make this work.

The points of difference do not seem to be relevant for recycling, and I will tell you why .

. .

When this same solution has been adopted elsewhere, it has worked.

In a parallel case . . .

Likewise . . .

Similarly . . .

REASONING CHECKLIST

Ask yourself the following questions when you start to develop your arguments and reason from your evidence. If you're still not clear on the main types of reasoning, make sure to carefully read chapter 16 in the text, or ask your instructor.

INDUCTIVE

Are the examples representative?

Are there enough examples to make a generalization?

Have you studied the examples well?

DEDUCTIVE

Are the underlying premises sound?

Does the conclusion necessarily follow from these premises?

Have the premises been clearly stated?

CAUSAL

Does the cause precede the effect?

Does the cause make a difference: If there were no cause, would the effect still happen?

Are there other factors contributing to the effect?

Have you mistaken coincidence for cause and effect?

ANALOGY

What is the comparison?

What are the similarities?

Is there a general principle that covers both sides?

Does the general principle really apply to both sides? What about differences?

REASONING FALLACIES

Hasty Generalization

A conclusion drawn on the basis of insufficient evidence.

> *All students are poor.*
> *You can't lose investing in technology stocks.*

Post Hoc or Doubtful Cause

Because one event follows another the first event must be the cause.

> *It rained because I washed my car.*
> *I have a good job because I went to college.*

Ad Hominem

An irrelevant attack on an opponent rather than his/her argument. The use of character assassination rather than solid refutation or persuasion.

> *His comments on feminist issues are irrelevant because he is a man and a stupid one if he thinks women are interested in what he has to say.*

False Dilemma or False Dichotomy

To base reasoning on an either/or statement when more than two alternatives exist.

> *Are we going to vote a pay increase for our teachers, or are we going to allow our schools to deteriorate into substandard custodial institutions?*

Slippery Slope

Objecting to a particular action on the grounds that once the action is taken, it will inevitably lead to a similar but less desirable action, which will lead to an even less desirable action, etc.

> *If we distribute needles to intravenous drug users, next thing you know we will be supplying them with drugs.*

Two Wrongs Make A Right

Justifying a wrong by claiming lots of people do the same thing.

> *Applied Widgets Inc. produces only half of the pollution of the company next door.*

Appeal to Tradition

What has existed for a long time should continue to exist because it is a tradition.

> *Why would I want to buy a Chevrolet, this family has always driven Fords.*

Maslow s Hierarchy of Needs

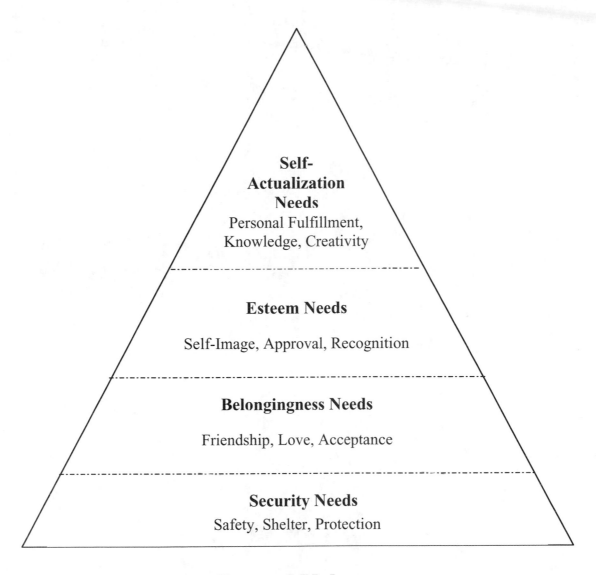

Self-Actualization Needs
Personal Fulfillment, Knowledge, Creativity

Esteem Needs

Self-Image, Approval, Recognition

Belongingness Needs

Friendship, Love, Acceptance

Security Needs
Safety, Shelter, Protection

General Values

Comfortable life
Exciting life
Sense of accomplishment
World at peace
World of beauty
Equality
Family security
Freedom
Happiness

Inner harmony
Mature love
National security
Pleasure
Salvation
Self-respect
Social recognition
True friendship
Wisdom

ADAPTING YOUR SPEECH TO A SPECIFIC AUDIENCE

Favorable Audience (Emphasis is on Pathos)

➢ Remind the audience why they agreed with you and motivate them to action.
➢ Use emotional appeals--appeal to their values and needs.
➢ Expand on your call to action--offer several alternatives; have them make a commitment and encourage them to get others involved.
➢ Make use of personal experiences; be creative (even involve the audience by asking them questions and letting them respond); use humor.
➢ You want to strengthen the audience attitude with a well-prepared and well organized speech. (Don t get over-confident and lazy.)

Neutral Audience (Use a balance of Ethos, Pathos, and Logos)

➢ There are different reasons why an audience might be neutral.
➢ For an uninterested audience:
  ▪ Work at getting their attention.
  ▪ Focus on how the issue affects them.
➢ For an uninformed audience:
  ▪ Explain issue; clarify confusing points.
  ▪ Use a lot of examples, definitions.
➢ For an informed, but undecided audience:
  ▪ Give both sides of argument.
  ▪ Include some new arguments or information.
  ▪ Your credibility is critical in this case.

Unfavorable Audience (Emphasize Logos and Ethos; use Pathos cautiously)

➢ Extensive evidence, Organization, Sound reasoning are important.
➢ Use expert data; cite your sources completely.
➢ Make sure your points are well supported.
➢ Stress common ground even though the audience may be unfavorable to your proposal; there may be certain values and concerns you have in common.
➢ Set realistic goals:
  ▪ Don t expect audience to act or even change their minds but be open to different perspectives.
  ▪ Prioritize your goals--focus on a couple of key points in your speech.
➢ Refute the opposing arguments without being judgmental and sarcastic:
  ▪ State the opposing argument fairly. State your position and document it with evidence. Then show how the two positions compare.
➢ Unfavorable audiences are usually skeptical of emotional appeals.
➢ Although you do not want to be combative, stay firm in your position!

PERSUASIVE (SPEECH #3) WORKSHEET

1. What is your thesis (proposition of public policy)?

2. What is the status quo (current situation) regarding your policy statement?

3. What is wrong with the status quo? Why do you want to make a change?

4. Whose domain is, or what public body is, responsible for upholding the status quo?

5. Who, what agent, would be able to make, or enact a change to the status quo?

6. What evidence and facts do you plan to provide to support your claim?

7. How does the above evidence support your claim? In other words, how will you turn your facts into reasoning?

8. What might be an argument against your proposition?

9. What are the possible main points for your speech?

SPEECH #3
PERSUASIVE SPEAKING

PURPOSE OF ASSIGNMENT:

This speech is designed to apply all of the concepts you have learned so far in this course. You will stay with your informative speech topic, using your peers feedback to craft a sound and effectively communicated persuasive argument. Your goal is to actually influence this audience in your desired direction. Your thesis should be stated as a proposition of public policy. In addition, you must call for a **direct and specific course of action** from your audience. Your speech is to be based on sound reasoning and evidence and must include motivational appeals and credibility.

REQUIREMENTS:

- Your topic should be one that is timely and one that you find very interesting.
- The speech should be **six to eight minutes** in length.
- The speech should be well-organized using the **Problem-Solution** or **Monroe s Motivated Sequence** patterns. The progression of ideas should be logical and the major points must stand out from the subpoints that develop them.
- You must use at least **one instance of valid reasoning**.
- You must use at least **two different methods to establish your credibility** with the audience. Label the dimension of credibility established (i.e., concern, competence, trustworthiness, dynamism).
- You must use at least **one appeal to audience needs**. Specify and **label** the specific need appealed to.
- You must use at least **one appeal to audience values**. Specify and **label** the specific value appealed to.
- Your style (language choice) should be clear, appropriate, vivid, and varied.
- Your delivery skills are to be the best so far extemporaneous, conversational, energetic, non-distracting . . . in short, persuasive.
- **Cite** at least **four sources** in your speech.
- A copy of your **typed, full-sentence** outline (following the correct format) is to be submitted on the day of your speech. The following elements are to be included and **labeled in the margin or where appropriate:**
  - Specific purpose & primary audience outcome
  - Thesis statement
  - Three functions of your introduction and conclusion
  - Transitions between main points
  - Two attempts to establish credibility
  - One appeal to audience needs
  - One appeal to audience values
  - One instance of valid reasoning
  - Four source citations in the text of the outline
  - A reference list in APA format with **at least four different** published source materials.
- **Bring your video tape** to the workshop per your instructor s request.

CRITERIA FOR EVALUATION:

To receive a passing grade for this assignment you need to make an earnest attempt at meeting the above requirements. In other words, if there are no serious deviations from the above requirements, expect to receive about 70% of the possible points (C range). If you not only meet the minimal requirements, but carry them out well, expect to receive 80-89% (B range) or, if you carry them out exceptionally well, expect to receive 90-100% (A range) of the possible points. Total points for the assignment will be weighted as follows:

Introduction	25 points
Organization	50 points
Development	50 points
Conclusion	25 points
Delivery	75 points
Total	**225 points**
Outline:	75 points possible

SUGGESTIONS FOR PREPARATION:

The largest amount of effort should go into developing the ideas you want to present. Make sure your main points clearly represent these ideas. Give special thought to your introduction and conclusion. These parts of your speech can make a strong impression that affects your persuasiveness.

Make use of supporting materials (i.e. statistics, definitions, testimony, examples). Begin your research as soon as possible so that you have plenty of time to consider how you want your speech to progress.

Review your video tape and decide which areas of delivery to be conscious of during the speech. **Practice aloud using your notecards and visual aids several times.** Work on really connecting with your audience. Move away from the lectern, maintain eye contact, show your sincerity in your face and voice.

On the day of the speech bring the following:

➤ Video tape per your instructor s request
➤ Your typed, full-sentence outline
➤ Notecards
➤ Evaluation Form

OUTLINE WORKSHEET

TOPIC:

ORGANIZATIONAL PATTERN:

SPECIFIC PURPOSE:

PRIMARY AUDIENCE OUTCOME:

THESIS STATEMENT (state central idea, the essence of the speech):

INTRODUCTION

ATTENTION GETTER:

PSYCHOLOGICAL ORIENTATION (relate topic to this audience):

LOGICAL ORIENTATION (state thesis, then preview main points):

BODY

•2-5 MAIN POINTS PREFERRED •USE ONLY COMPLETE SENTENCES

I.   MAIN POINT (state as a single declarative sentence):

   A.   SUBPOINT:

      1.
            a.
            b.
      2.
            a.
            b.

   B.   SUBPOINT:

1.
    a.
    b.
2.
    a.
    b.

C.   SUBPOINT:

1.
    a.
    b.
2.
    a.
    b.

Transition:

II.   MAIN POINT (state as a single declarative sentence):

A.   SUBPOINT:

1.
    a.
    b.
2.
    a.
    b.

B.   SUBPOINT:

1.
    a.
    b.
2.
    a.
    b.

C.   SUBPOINT:

1.
    a.
    b.
2.
    a.

b.

III.   MAIN POINT (state as a single declarative sentence):

    A.   SUBPOINT:

        1.

            a.
            b.

        2.

            a.
            b.

    B.   SUBPOINT:

        1.

            a.
            b.

        2.

            a.
            b.

    C.   SUBPOINT:

        1.

            a.
            b.

        2.

            a.
            b.

CONCLUSION

LOGICAL CLOSURE (restate main points and thesis):

PSYCHOLOGICAL CLOSURE (relate importance and relevance to this audience):

CLINCHER (end with a bang, not a whimper):

SPEECH #3 TIPS

Following is a checklist that you can use to make sure that you are meeting the requirements for Speech 3. This is your final speech. That means that I expect exceptional work. This speech should reflect the entire semester s worth of concepts and feedback. **Before** you hand in your speech, make sure that you have checked these details.

Outline

- Do you have statistics, definitions, testimonial or examples as main points (I level), or as A level points? (You absolutely should not. These supporting materials belong at the #1 or a level. They *support* your major arguments.)

- Are you using full, complete, declarative sentences? No questions? No phrases?

- Have you proofread thoroughly and had someone else proofread as well? (Checking for grammatical and spelling errors, as well as for appropriate spacing, tabs and indentation?)

- Have you **cited all of your sources in the text**? (Do not put a source in your reference list unless you have cited it in text.)

- Are your sources cited in proper APA format?

- Is the *kind* of reasoning that you use clearly identified? Are you sure?

- Is the need (from Maslow) and the value (from Rokeach) listed?

- Is your thesis sentence worded as a should statement? Is it clearly **public policy**?

Content

- Does every main point that you make tie back to your thesis sentence?

- Is each point developed appropriately?

- Do you incorporate a variety of sources?

- Do you address counter arguments?

- Have you included something that will get the audience s attention?

- Have you given them a compelling reason to listen? Have you related the topic to *their* needs and *their* experiences?

- Have you summarized your main points?

- Have you included a clear call to action?

Delivery

- Have you practiced enough?
- Are you speaking extemporaneously?
- Do you really know the intricacies of your topic?
- Have you visualized yourself as a dynamic speaker?
- Is your visual aid clear? Readable? Does it clarify complex material?
- Do you use visual aids in every place where they will clarify complex material or help your audience understand you better?

Credibility

- Have you cited your sources to establish your credibility?
- Do you really know your topic? Do you have additional sources to investigate?
- Do you address counter arguments?
- Are you prepared to answer audience questions about your topic?

Transitions/Reasoning

- Have you made your reasoning *very* clear to your audience?
- Have you interpreted your statistics?
- Have you utilized emphasis cues and repetition to make sure that the audience remembers your most important points?

Speech 3: PersuasiveSpeech

Introduction: _____ Strengths: _____ ?s/suggestions/not-so-strengths _____

Attention-getting Material
_____ out of 5 pts possible

Thematic statement
_____ out of 10 pts possible

Preview
_____ out of 5 pts possible

Establishing credibility
_____ out of 5 pts possible

Organization: _____ Strengths: _____ ?s/suggestions/not-so-strengths _____

Logical organization
_____ out of 50 pts possible

Development _____ Strengths: _____ ?s/suggestions/not-so-strengths _____

Appropriate development
_____ out of 50 pts possible

Conclusion: _____ Strengths: _____ ?s/suggestions/not-so-strengths _____

Summary/Review
_____ out of 10 pts possible

Closure
_____ out of 15 pts possible

Delivery: _____ Strengths: _____ ?s/suggestions/not-so-strengths: _____

Effective extemporaneous delivery
_____ out of 75 pts possible

Total: _____ out of 225 points possible; Grade: _____

Outline: _____ out of 75 points possible
Peer Feedback: _____ out of 20 points possible

Peer Feedback Form

Speaker: _____   Respondent: _____

1=missing   2=average   3=good   4=excellent

Introduction:

Attention-getter effectiveness   1   2   3   4

Thesis   1   2   3   4

    What was the thesis? _____

Establishing credibility   1   2   3   4

Body:

    What were the main points?: _____
_____
_____
_____
_____

Organized Effectively   1   2   3   4

Sufficient Development   1   2   3   4

Effective Use of Transitions?   1   2   3   4

Conclusion:

Summary/Review   1   2   3   4

Closure   1   2   3   4

    Were you left with a lasting impression? What was it?:

    Write at least one question to ask the speaker when s/he has concluded:

    Note at least two strengths of this presentation:

    Note one or two areas for improvement:

Reading Guide for Listening

(Chapter 2)

Finish this sentence:

A message does not really exist until it is <u>received</u> and <u>shaped</u> by a listener.

List and explain three ways you show you are curious yet critical:

1. Be open to the speakers point of view. Try not to be too critical about a person's speech topic. Be polite.

2. Critically assess the speakers claims. Think about how true the person's argument is.

3. Ask questions. At designated times ask questions to show you're interested.

Using principles for constructive feedback revise the following comment. Explain which principles you used and why you used them.

You spoke to rapidly! There's no way I can hear what you are saying if you ramble it off ridiculously fast!

I enjoyed the topic of your speach. It was very original. Next time try to talk a little slower so you will be heard more easily.

- The 90/10 principle & give suggestions, not orders

Which listening pitfall(s) do you find tend to fall into? What can you do to break the habit?

I tend to daydream and disengage myself from the speech. To break that habit I can force myself to pay attention by taking notes.

Reading Guide for Speaking Ethics
(Chapter 3)

The text says you need to, recognize that every action has an ethical dimension. In your own words, what do they mean?

They mean that everytime you make a speech you have an opportunity to convince people that what you feel about a subject is correct.

How can you show that you are respecting your personal integrity when speaking in front of our class?

You can show your personal integrity by always speaking from your heart and saying how you feel not what everyone wants to hear.

Of course, plagiarism is not tolerated on the SJSU campus. What is plagiarism and how can it take form in a speech (list 2)?

Plagiarism is when you take someone else's ideas and use them as your own. It can appear in a speech if you use a quote, but don't state the source. It is also plagiarism if you use someone else's outline on a speech.

Have you ever witnessed someone who got caught for plagiarism? What happened? How serious were the consequences?

I have never known anyone who got caught for plagiarism.

What should we expect from the public speakers in our class? Create you own list of ethical expectations for our class.

I expect people to be polite and courteous to the speaker. I expect them to act interested and not talk during a presentation and to applaud at the end.

Reading Guide for Overcoming Fear of Speaking
(Chapter 4)

List all the fears you currently have about public speaking:

I am afraid of someone answering a question I can't answer and of stumbling over my words or losing my place.

Choose your top two fears and analyze where those fears come from. What are you scared will happen? Did something happen in the past to make you feel the way you do?

I am afraid of someone answering a question I can't answer because I have seen it happen to other people before and was scared for them. I don't want to stumble over my words because that makes you look nervous. Nothing negative has ever happened to me before though.

Finish the following sentences:

People who perform in the public eye actors, athletes, musicians and speakers have learned to _function_ while concealing their _fear_.

Remind yourself that an audience is merely a group of _individuals_ and that a speech is merely an _enlarged conversation_

Of all the techniques discussed in the text, which three do you think will be most helpful for you and overcoming your fears? How will they make you feel more confident?

I think, if I replace negative feeling with positive ones I will be reassuring myself. I think taking a little walk will help me to relax before a speech. I also think if I practice the speech a lot it will make me more confident beforehand.

Reading Guide for Planning

(Chapter 5)

List the four phases of creativity and describe what happens at each phase:

1. Preperation - You figure out your audience, gather some materials and decide on a topic

2. Incubation- If you get stuck set it aside and you will unconsciously be working on a solution to the problem

3. Illumination - Everything comes together and works itself out.

4. Refinement - this is when you check your facts & make sure everything is true and you make sure you have everything you need.

Finish the sentence:

When setting a timetable for preparing your speech, always provide _extra time_

time for _emergencies_

Do you think making a task completion timetable would help you stay on track with your speech creation process? Why?

It might help a little, but usually when I work on a project I like to do it all at once.

Which planning pitfall do you usually get into? How has it affected your work in the past? What will you do to avoid falling into the same pitfall again?

I don't leave much time for incubation, I like to finish all at once. I can come up with idea and let it set in for a while and then finish it up.

Reading Guide for Topic Selection and Analysis
(Chapter 6)

What should you always draw from when choosing a speech topic? Give examples.

You should always draw from something you know.
Talk about your experiences, topics that you have
strong opinions on a topic or on your
expertises and things you know best.

What are some speech topics you are sick of hearing or feel are boring?

I am tired of hearing about abortion,
drugs, and drinking.

What does it mean to choose a topic that is timely and timeless ?

It means to choose a topic that people
can relate to no matter what time
period they live in.

Why is it important to narrow your topic? What happens if you don t narrow your topic enough?

It is important to narrow your topic so you know
how much time you have left. If you don't narrow
your topic you can end up giving only superficial
information with no depth.

What is the difference between a speech to inform and a speech to persuade?

A speech to inform mainly describes or explains
a topic, but a speech to persuade tries to
convince or sway the listeners of your point
of view.

Reading Guide for Audience Analysis
(Chapter 7)

Fill in the sentence:

Speakers do not give speeches ___to___ audiences; they ___jointly___ create

meaning ___with___ audiences.

What are demographic characteristics?

They are characteristics that describe an audience.
like age, race, occupation, and religion.

List at least 4 areas of demographic information. Why is each important to consider?

Age- a teenager will probably not care about one topic, but an adult would.

gender- you don't want to insult males/females by discussing something like gender roles

Race- ethnic diversity can be a good thing or bad.

Sexual breakdown- You never want to insult anyone such as giving a speech about homosexual marriage.

What happens when a speaker doesn t think about what is meaningful to his/her audience?

If a speaker doesn't consider his audience he could end up insulting an individual or the whole audience.

What are some questions a speaker should ask about his/her speech topic before constructing the speech?

What do they know about the topic you chose

What do they know about you as a person?

What does your audience think?

What is their history?

Where does your speech topic fit in with your Audience?

Reading Guide for Research
(Chapter 8)

What resources have you used for doing research in the library?

I have pretty much only used books from the library.

What resources would you like to learn more about?

Periodicals

Who do you know that may be able to serve as a resource for you in your upcoming speech?

I could use a professional such as a coach, a doctor, or someone like that.

Choose a book from your personal collection, a text book, or any one from the library. Below, cite the book in proper APA format.

Sprague, Jo, Stuart, Douglas. (2005). "The Speakers Handbook." Belmont: Thomson Wadsworth.

Think about your next speech topic what questions might your audience have about your topic? How will this guide your future research?

What are some of the rules of the sport? What is your background in the sport? Any advice?

Reading Guide for Transforming Ideas into Speech Points
(Chapter 9)

Fill in the stages you would follow to come up with speech points:

1.

2.

3.

4.

Now, brainstorm on the topic you think you are going to speak about for your next speech:

$$\boxed{}$$

Do you see logical categories emerging from the brain storm you did above? What are the categories you think could work?

What does mutually exclusive mean? Provide an example.

Reading Guide for Arranging Points
(Chapter 10)

Give 2 examples of speech topics that benefit from a chronological organizational pattern.

1.

2.

Give 2 examples of speech topics that benefit from a spatial organizational pattern.

1.

2.

Why would you use a cause-effect pattern? Give an example of a speech topic that would benefit from this pattern.

Which kind of speech uses the problem-solution pattern? Why would you use this pattern?

Why would you use a topical organizational pattern?

Reading Guide for Outlining
(Chapter 11)

What does the act of outlining force you to do?

Write in the proper roman numeral/symbol for the type of idea given:

_____ First Main Point

_____ First Level of Subordination

_____ Second Level of Subordination

_____ Third Level of Subordination

_____ Fourth Level of Subordination

Fill in the sentence:

Each subordinate idea should be _____ several spaces to align with the _____--not the labeling numeral or letter of the point it supports. This makes the relationship among ideas visually obvious.

What is the general rule when developing a level of subordination? Why is this a rule?

Explain how the True/False test works.

How many ideas should you have for any given symbol in your outline?

Reading Guide for Transitions
(Chapter 12)

Why are transitions necessary?

List all the transitional words you can think of in the box below:

```



```

What is an internal summary and a internal preview? How are they different than regular transitions?

Use a transition to link the following topics:

Fall   *Spring*
Transition:

McDonald's   *Taco Bell*
Transition:

Punk   *Hip-Hop*
Transition:

Reading Guide for Introductions
(Chapter 13)

List the four necessary parts of any speech introduction:

1.

2.

3.

4.

Create two different attention getters you might consider using for your next speech.

1.

2.

What is the difference between the logical orientation and the psychological orientation?

Fill in the sentence:

"Generally, your introduction should take up _____-_____% of your speaking time."

What are the questions you should keep in mind and answer when constructing your introduction?

Reading Guide for Conclusions
(Chapter 14)

What are the three necessary parts of the conclusion?:

1.

2.

3.

It's important to end your speech on a strong note. What shouldn't you say when ending your speech?

Look at the common conclusion pitfalls on page 167. Which ones do you find yourself doing? What will you do to keep yourself from those pitfalls? (Choose at least 2).

Reading Guide for Supporting Materials
(Chapter 15)

Finish the sentence:

They probably _____ whether your _____ characterize your utterances as _____ or _____, _____ or _____."

Make a list of unfamiliar terms you may use in your next speech.   Next to each one, explain what type of definition you could use to enlighten your audience.

    1.

    2.

    3.

    4.

Why is it important to give examples when you speak?

What additional information would you need to have before accepting the following statistical evidence?

"Studies show that over two thirds of the total meaning a person communicates is conveyed nonverbally."

List or create several lead-ins you would use when introducing a supporting material when speaking.

-
-

Reading Guide for Reasoning

Chapter 16

What is a claim?

Fill in the blanks:

"Your _____ is a claim, you _____ _____ are claims that support that claim, and even some of your _____ _____ have to be reasoned through before they become acceptable."

Under what conditions would a speaker consider using inductive reasoning?

Think of a speech topic that would benefit from deductive reasoning.

What is another name for "Causal" reasoning?

Use reasoning by analogy to compare a family and a group of employees.

Reading Guide for Language & Style
(Chapter 17)

Compare/contrast oral style from written style:

Oral Style:	Written Style:

How could you rephrase the following commonly used jargon/slang terms to sound more appropriate for a speech?

and, like .

um

hella

you guys

Fill in the blanks:

Referring to a group or individuals by the _____ _____

_____ is a sign of _____

Reading Guide for Attention and Interest

(Chapter 18)

Fill in the blanks:

Never say _____ or _____ if you can give a name

Why is this so?

How can you enliven your speech up throughout your speech? Discuss at least 5 different ways!

Describe how you could use at least 3 of the attention getters from 18A in a speech on the topic of Electric and Hybrid Vehicles :

Reading Guide for Credibility

Chapter 19

How do you personally determine if another person is credible?

Fill in the blanks:

If a speaker is energetic, uses colorful language, and leads their audience confidently

through their speech they may be considered a _____ speaker.

When a speaker is friendly and continuously addresses their audience s needs they are

concerned with their _____   _____.

If you are giving a speech about why high school standardized testing should be eliminated , what can you say to be perceived as trustworthy?

Finish this sentence:
To communicate a sense of expertise, you must let listeners know you have

_____.

Name 5 ways you will show your credibility while speaking to our class:

Reading Guide for Motivational Appeals

(Chapter 20)

Label the levels of Maslow's Hierarchy of Needs:

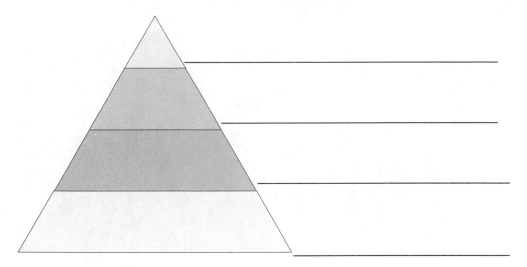

Fill in the ranking of values:

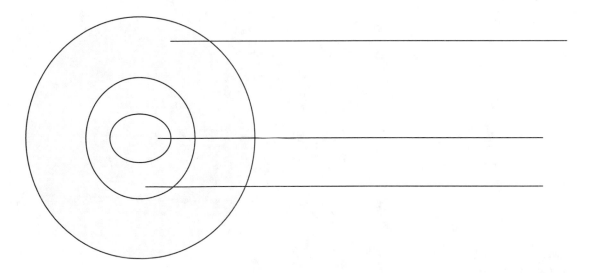

Reading Guide for Informative Strategies
(Chapter 21)

What is information overload? Explain a time when you experienced this.

Use your next speech topic to explain how you will move your topic from the simple to the complex.

Which principles of clear explanation do you want to include more of in your next speech? Why?

Reading Guide for Persuasive Strategies
(Chapter 22)

What are your persuasive goals for your next speech?

Identify which of the following are propositions of fact, value, or policy:
Music on MTV is simplistic and tasteless.

Proposition of _____

Cats make better pets than dogs.

Proposition of _____

Write a proposition of fact, value, and policy on the following general topic:

Women in the Military

Fact:

Value:

Policy:

List and explain the five steps of Monroe s Motivated Sequence:
1.

2.

3.

4.

5.

Reading Guide for Adapting to Speaking Contexts
(Chapter 23)

What is the difference between a formal demeanor and an informal demeanor? How does our classroom context rank on the continuum of formal and informal demeanor?

What is the difference between highly proscribed rules of speaking and more open rules of speaking? What are the rules of speaking in our classroom context?

What future public speeches/presentations do you see yourself encountering? How will you adapt what you are learning in this class to your future context?

READING GUIDE FOR MODES OF DELIVERY
(Chapter 24)

What are the four modes of delivery? How does each one work?

1. Impromptu- Nothing to go off of. Improv.

2. Extemporaneous- You have notes to speak off of.

3. Manuscript - You write out everything you are going to say & read it off of a paper.

4. memorized - You memorize exactly what you are going to say beforehand and recite it when the time comes.

Why should you use the extemporaneous mode of delivery most of the time?

You should use this mode most of the time because you prepare extensively, yet still have a little room for spontaneity.

Finish the sentence:

But even for the occasional public speaker, the <u>extemporaneous</u> mode, once

mastered, gives a sense of <u>power</u> and <u>confidence</u>.

What is the difference between destructive feedback and constructive/effective feedback?

Fill in the blanks:

Doing a stand-up, full-scale practice _____ in the morning and _____ in the

evening for _____ days is _____ better than running through

the speech six times in a row.

It is our opinion that _____ in front of a _____ often does

more _____ than _____.

What are a few things you would do if you speech was too long?:

What would you do if your speech was too short?

Reading Guide for Vocal Delivery
(Chapter 26)

What are a few areas you feel you should work on to improve your vocal delivery?

What does the text say about the areas you want to improve?

What are you telling your audience if you speak in a monotone voice?

What steps should you take if you want to set up your own self-improvement program?

1.

2.

3.

Reading Guide for Physical Delivery
(Chapter 27)

How can you show your audience you are conscious of your appearance?

If you tend to use a distracting mannerism when speaking what can you do?

Tell me what gesture-inhibiting stance you see speakers using the most. What message does it send to an audience member?

What does eye contact signal to audience members in the American culture?

What happens if you do not give your audience enough eye contact?

Finish the sentence:

A _____ _____ is best used in two places: when you are

attempting to explain a _____ or _____ idea and when you

want to _____ a particular message.

What are some guidelines to follow when creating a visual aid?

What should you do when using your visual aid during your speech?

What are some complications you may run into if you chose to use a technologically savvy visual aid?

Reading Guide for Adapting to the Speech Situation
(Chapter 29)

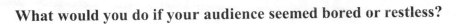

What would you do if your audience seemed bored or restless?

What can you do to deal with distractions during your speech?

What is a "heckler"? What can you do if you encounter a heckler?

Employee Privacy and the Internet
Outline of a Persuasive Speech (Chapters 17 and 18)

Chris Farthing

Chris's assignment was to prepare and deliver a persuasive speech in the general topic area of electronic media.

Topic: Employee Privacy and the Internet
General Purpose: To persuade

Specific Purpose: To persuade my audience that companies deserve the right to monitor their employees' use of the Internet, email, and instant messenger services.

Central Idea: Companies own the equipment and they are paying for employees' time; therefore they have the right to monitor employees' time, but employees can protect themselves.

Introduction

I. Imagine Cheryl: she uses her coffee break to search the Internet for information about a cousin's health problems; her employee monitors this search and contacts the Human Resources Department, which records these visits in Cheryl's insurance files.

II. Any time you go to work, either now or in the future, your employer has the right to monitor your computer usage.

III. At a Web development company where I previously worked, two coworkers were reprimanded for misusing company time after they sent several inappropriate emails back and forth and surfed the Internet on company time.

IV. Today, I will summarize the history of Internet privacy issues, explain why employers should be allowed to monitor employees, describe what employers should do for employees, and finally tell what employees can do to protect themselves.

Body

I. Internet privacy and the workplace first became a major issue when the Internet became an increasingly popular way of communicating and doing business.

  A. Informationweek.com says, "When monitoring started to catch on a few years ago, it was in response to several high-profile sexual harassment cases. Now, employers are increasingly concerned about productivity and bandwidth."

    1. Employees download pornographic material from the Internet and cause a hostile environment for other employees who are subjected to unwanted images; they also send harassing messages to coworkers.

      a. SexTracker, a site that monitors pornography site usage, reports that 70 percent of porn traffic occurs during business hours (networkmagazine.com).

      b. The same source defines harassment as sexual, hateful, prejudicial, or inflammatory email.

    2. Networkmagazine.com also says, "Since the Industrial Revolution began and factories sprang up, productivity has become the god of industry. And if productivity is god, then the greatest sin one can commit is wasting time."

    3. As the Internet grew, employees began to download music, read news, and watch streaming videos, which greatly slowed down company networks, forcing them to pay for more bandwidth.

  B. Employers are legally allowed to monitor everything on company computers.

    1. CNN.com says, "U.S. law, which is backed by court rulings, makes clear that 'he who owns the computers gets to see what is going on with their computers,' he said."

    2. Instant messaging is currently the only safe haven for private communication, but soon even that will be open to scrutiny.

  C. Monitoring employees is a fast growing industry.

    1. Wired.com reports, "International Data Corporation (IDC) estimates that corporations worldwide spent $62 million on Internet filtering and monitoring software in 1999. An IDC study predicts that figure will rise to $561 million by 2005."

2. Msnbc.com says, "Interest in IM monitoring is soaring as companies not only look to record important communications but also control information leaks and discourage cyber slacking."

II. Companies own the employees' equipment and time; therefore, they should be able to monitor both as much or as little as they see fit.

A. Businesses want to know if people are doing anything illegal with company property.

1. Harassment—sexual or otherwise—is an example.
2. Illegally selling company secrets is another reason to monitor.
3. If I own something, I should be able to monitor my own property.

B. As long as employees are on a time clock, the company has the right to know what they are doing with their time.

1. Businesses want to know if people are using their time efficiently or slacking off.
2. Msnbc.com gives an illustration of wasted time, "If an employee surfs the Internet just 5 minutes of every hour at a pay of $15 per hour the loss to a business can be enormous. An eight-hour day has 40 minutes wasted, which becomes 200 minutes per week. At 48 weeks a year (4 allotted for vacation and sick time) that is 160 hours. This translates into $2400 on a single employee. For a business with only 500 personnel using computers that is $1,200,000."

III. Although they have the right to monitor employees, employers who want their employees' respect and loyalty should not abuse this tool.

A. Employers often expect more out of their employees, demanding long hours and stressful working conditions.
B. In order to allow employees to take care of personal needs, many businesses overlook limited personal emails and quick checks of personal information on the Internet.

1. Employees can go online during breaks and check personal stocks, read news, or even chat online for a short time.
2. Andrew Meyer of Websense, a company that makes Internet filtering software, explains, "If it's easier for me to do a five-minute, online banking transaction, it's a lot better than if I have to get in my car, go out to the bank, and spend 20 minutes in line" (networkmagazine.com).

C. Employers should also make plain their policy on use of company equipment and time so that employees know what is expected and can work accordingly.

IV. Employees can protect themselves from discipline by keeping their actions in line with their company's policy.

A. Make it a point to know your company's view toward using its time and network for your personal use.
B. If you are unsure of whether or not something is appropriate to do on a company computer, go and ask your supervisor.
C. If you don't think it's something you can discuss with your supervisor, you probably shouldn't do it at work.

Conclusion

I. Today we have discussed why businesses have the right to monitor their employees' actions on the Internet and on company computers.

II. We went over how Internet monitoring developed, why it is legal and appropriate, what businesses should do for their employees, and finally what you can do to protect yourself.

III. When you are using a work computer, hopefully you will stop to think that your company may be legally monitoring you, but as long as you are doing what you are supposed to do with company time and property, this should not cause pain or anxiety.

IV. But if Cheryl had thought through the implications of Internet monitoring, she might have done her research away from the workplace.

Embryo Adoption
A Persuasive Speech (Chapters 17 and 18)

Paul Southwick

Paul prepared this speech when he was a competitor on his speech team at Clackamas Community College. He delivered it at regional and national tournaments, and often took home a trophy. You can watch this speech under Speech Interactive for Chapter 4 on your Jaffe Connection CD-ROM.

There is something magical and beautiful that happens every winter, if we are lucky; snow. Thousands of snowflakes cover the ground and each snowflake is unique from the rest. Now, there is a new type of snowflake that science has led us to marvel at, the human embryo. Each little embryo is unique from the rest and is a mysterious new life beginning to grow. As *Citizen Magazine* reports in the October 2001 edition, Hannah Sterge, now a rambunctious two-year-old, was one of these snowflakes. The Nightlight Christian Adoption Agency in Fullerton California gave embryo adoptees this wintry name because the embryos are frozen and no two are alike.

However, a large amount of heat is threatening the existence of little snowflakes across the country. Many lobbyists are continuing to pressure the government for additional funding to obtain, destroy, and research on tiny, unsuspecting victims like Hannah Sterge. The United States government should discontinue its embryonic stem cell research and increase the funding for adult stem cell research.

Through the next few minutes we will examine the humanness of the embryo, then uncover the fallacies of embryonic stem cells, and finally slide into the benefits of adult stem cell research.

First, we will examine the humanness of the embryo. Many, including biologist Irv Weissman of Stanford University in a July 9th, 2001, *Newsweek* article, have treated the human embryo as merely a piece of tissue or lifeless substance. However, peering through medical history and concluding with medical expertise from our own time we will see that a human embryo is life in its most basic stage. Beginning with Dr. Bradley M. Patten's 1963 textbook, *Human Embryology*, we find that the culmination of the process of fertilization marks the initiation of the life of a new individual. Moving farther along in the timeline, in 1980 Dr. Jerome LeJeune, world renowned genetics professor, revealed that after fertilization has taken place a new human being has come into existence. Recent embryologists echo the words of Dr. Patten and Dr. LeJeune. Dr. C. Ward Kischer, professor at the University of Arizona college of Medicine, states in a July 16th, 2001, article that "The life of the new individual human being begins at fertilization. . . . Every human embryologist, world wide, know this . . . and it is so stated in virtually every textbook of human embryology."

At the June 2001 National Right to Life Convention in North Carolina, a lecture was given on human development. The lecture pertained to women who saw pictures of their unborn child at its earliest stage of development, mentioning that the child looked like a blob or a tadpole. The lecture affirmed the women; don't worry. That little blob in your

tummy isn't going to be frog, a chicken, or a giraffe. It's a little human and its just going to get bigger. Since we know that the embryo is human, we should protect it.

After all, as Sen. Brownback of Kansas in the December 8th, 2001, issue of *World Magazine* points out regarding endangered-species laws, "You can't touch a bald eagle's eggs. You can't even mess with their habitat." As a society, we have recognized the importance of the beginnings of animal life, and it is time to recognize the importance of early human life as well.

Now that we have discovered the humanness of the embryo, wisdom's call beckons us to uncover the fallacies of embryonic stem cell research.

Many, including the National Institutes of Health and numerous mainstream media, are treating embryonic stem cells as a miraculous cure. Whether the cells are derived from unused embryos at in vitro fertilization clinics or as we have seen recently, through embryonic cloning, the hope of many science and research universities, like Johns Hopkins University, is that embryonic stem cells will one day be able to cure degenerative diseases like Alzheimer's and Parkinson's disease.

However, editorial page writer Richard Miniter, in the September 9th, 2001, edition of *Forbes Magazine*, reveals the reality of the situation, labeling embryonic stem cell research as "shaky" and "speculative." Mr. Miniter states bluntly and accurately that "[e]mbryonic stem cells have yet to save a single life." He credits researchers' demands for federal funding as stemming from the lack of private funding due to biotech companies viewing embryonic stem cell research as unprofitable.

Another complication with embryonic stem cell research is the high probability that transplanted embryonic cells will be rejected by the recipient. In July of 2001 Doctor Lauren Pecorino labeled immune rejection as a possible disadvantage to embryonic stem cells. Immune rejection is a large disadvantage because cells derived from an embryo may have a different immune profile than the person the cells would be transferred to, causing cell rejection.

Finally, we must uncover the fallacy that embryonic stem cell research does not destroy a human life. Though small, this human embryo will eventually grow into a fetus, then an infant, where the child will continue to grow and enter preschool like Hannah Sterge. Next, little Hannah will go through all the changes of puberty, go to college, possibly fall in love, get married, join the workforce, have kids, travel, and enjoy all that life has to offer. Unless, of course, life is cut off at its most basic stage and everything that follows is erased.

During the June 28th edition of *Fox News Sunday* one of embryonic stem cell research's proponents, Sen. Orrin Hatch from Utah, claimed that "an embryo in a petri dish is not a human life." Dr. Kischer profoundly asks the opposing question, is an embryo in a petri dish a human death? Of course not! "It is still a life process, but one that has been artificially suspended. This does not alter the integrity of the life process unless the manipulation is destructive."

Thankfully, there is a strong beacon of hope in the fact that adult stem cells are actively curing people and contain the promise of curing further degenerative diseases, without the destruction of a human life.

Adult stem cells are derived, without harm, from an individual and are naturally accepted and grown within that individual's system. In an October 2001 *Citizen Magazine* article, Michael Fumento, a science journalist and senior fellow at the Hudson Institute, states that there are many locations of adult stem cells, including bone marrow, newborns' umbilical cords, placentas, fat tissue, and virtually every part of the human body. Furthermore, a January 23rd, 2002, article in *New Scientist* reveals the eye-opening discovery of an adult stem cell that can turn into every single tissue in the body: muscle, cartilage, bone, liver, and different types of neurons. Additionally, the *Boston Globe* reported on January 24th, 2002, that some adult stem cell lines have grown in culture for two years and

show no signs of aging. Though this discovery is very new and must still be confirmed by colleagues, Morphogen Pharmaceuticals Incorporated of San Diego has revealed similar results, and many more groups will likely follow suit.

Unlike embryonic stem cells, in recent months adult stem cells have cured a disease. On January 24th, 2002, *HealthScoutNews* reported that an early adult stem cell therapy cured "Bubble Boy" disease, a disorder that erases the immune system. Even more exciting is the scientific potential for adult stem cells to treat and cure heart disease, sickle cell anemia, radiation sickness, Parkinson's disease, and many others.

The greatest benefit of adult stem cell research and therapy is that human lives are not sacrificed. Contrary to popular belief, a large portion of people who could benefit from embryonic stem cell research are opposing the research on ethical grounds. An October 2001 *Citizen Magazine* article reveals two of these people as Andrew Sullivan and Mark Pickup. Andrew Sullivan is an HIV-infected journalist who contends, "If my life were extended one day at the expense of one other human's life, it would be an evil beyond measure." Another candidate for embryonic stem cell research, Mark Pickup, was tragically diagnosed with multiple sclerosis and is now confined to a wheelchair. Mark admits that sometimes it is tempting to wish that embryonic stem cell research could one day make him able to walk again, but he realizes something that many people have ignored. In Mark's own words, "To gain my freedom from disease, I would become more wretched by accepting the fruits of robbing another of life, existence and a place in the world. No! The cure would only increase the torment." Let us stand with Andrew Sullivan and Mark Pickup, rejecting life-destroying embryonic stem cell research while encouraging the development of life-giving adult stem cells, which every human being has been given.

Today, we have examined the humanness of the embryo, then uncovered the fallacies of embryonic stem cells, and finally slid into the benefits of adult stem cell research.

In order to take a step in the protection of human lives in the embryonic state, we can choose to accept the scientific and ethical support that human embryos are lives that deserve protection. Also, our government should encourage embryo adoption. This will ensure that every embryo has the chance to keep on living. Finally, our nation must take a larger stride in the exploration and development of adult stem cell research, which will keep little human embryos like Hannah Sterge alive, as well as finding very possible cures to degenerative diseases. When all is said and done on the embryonic stem cell research debate, we must look for wisdom from Dr. Suess who wrote, "A person's a person. No matter how small." In our case, even when they are the size of a snowflake.

The following speeches, both on the same subject, show how differently two people approach a topic depending on their purpose, their audience, and the context in which they speak. Angela prepared her speech for the classroom and delivered it extemporaneously on one occasion. Sonja prepared hers for competition in intercollegiate speech tournaments; she memorized it and gave it many times during the year.

Sleep Deprivation
A Persuasive Speech Outline (Chapters 17 and 18)

Angela Wilson

General Purpose: To persuade
Specific Purpose: To persuade (convince) my audience that sleep deprivation has three negative consequences.
Central Idea: When sleep is deprived, individuals suffer financially and relationally, and society as a whole suffers.

Introduction

I. We need food, water, shelter . . . and sleep to survive.

II. We are similar to rats in our need for sleep; without food, rats last sixteen days; without sleep they last only seventeen days.

III. As I began to study the effects of sleep deprivation on society, I found many interesting facts.

IV. Sleep deprivation affects society in three specific ways: our financial lives, our personal relationships, and our work environments all suffer.

Body

I. First of all, sleep deprivation affects us financially.

   A. Americans waste $70 billion a year in lost productivity, accidents, and medical bills.

   B. Americans fill over 14 million prescriptions a year to help them sleep; they also spend millions on OTC drugs, 33 million in grocery stores.

   C. In 1977 there were three sleep disorder clinics, now there are 377; we waste billions of dollars and hundreds of hours of labor building clinics because we aren't sleeping right.

II. Second, sleep deprivation affects our individual relationships.

   A. Because society is made up of interrelated individuals, when one person struggles, we all do.

   B. When sleep deprived, individuals have trouble controlling their emotions and behaviors.

      1. Small disagreements can become potentially explosive.

      2. Sleep deprivation leaves us feeling sluggish, tired, irritable, and depressed.

      3. Volunteers in an experiment, after going sleepless for some time, exhibited childish, masochistic, and paranoid behaviors; they also injured themselves.

      4. Sleep deprived individuals have increasingly aggressive behaviors.

III. And finally, sleep deprivation affects safety in our working environments.

   A. Volunteers, who were asked to refrain from sleeping for a certain amount of time, became listless, serious, and grim; they did poorly on tasks of vigilance, reaction time, and simple arithmetic.

      1. Imagine yourself as a truck driver, a fireman, or a schoolteacher.

      2. All of these jobs require vigilance, reaction time, and simple arithmetic skills.

   B. Examples of lives lost due to sleep deprivation are those of the *Challenger* space shuttle and Exxon *Valdez* oil spill.

Conclusion

I. In conclusion, I ask you to consider the facts and statistics I have presented.

II. Sleep deprivation really is a factor that affects our work, our personal relationships, and our lives.

III. Let those poor research rats be a warning to you, and go get some sleep!

Sleep Deprivation

A Persuasive Speech (Chapters 17 and 18)

Sonja Ralston

Since Congress has finally achieved a budget surplus, they've been able to devote their time to more important things, like declaring this week National Sleep Awareness Week. The

March 22, 1999, *USA Today* in part of a nineteen-article series on sleep deprivation warned that we are faced with a new national debt measured, not in dollars, but in lost hours of sleep.

William Dement, a sleep researcher at Stanford University, explains that a sleep debt accumulates night after night. if you skip one hour a night for eight nights, you'll owe your body as if you had stayed up all night long. And if you think only college students carry a sleep balance (akin to their credit card balance) somewhere deep in the red, keep in mind that James B. Mass, a sleep researcher at Cornell University, noted in the May 27, 1998, *Houston Chronicle*, "It's a national crisis." And it's affecting more than just our moods; every year the national sleep debt costs us $166 billion and 13,000 lives.

Before we can drift off for a good night's sleep we must first wake up to some of the alarming effects of sleep debts, then we can open our eyes to better understand their causes, and finally cozy up to some solutions at both the personal and the societal levels.

Unlike your loan shark, Big Tony, when you default on a debt to your body it can't exactly smash your kneecaps with a baseball bat. Instead it retaliates with the effects of sleep debts, which range from general fatigue to something as fatal as sleeping behind the wheel, and everything in between.

According to the December 12, 1998, edition of the *Tokyo Daily*, those most severely affected are "shift workers, parents of young children, and young adults, most notably students." However, it can affect anyone, especially those with high levels of stress in their lives, and according to a survey released last week by the National Sleep Foundation, 65 percent of adults are suffering from sleep deprivation, more than twice the number reported in 1991.

According to the *Orange County Register* of September 12, 1998, "an estimated 23 million Americans are afflicted with migraine headaches," the most common cause of which is a basic lack of sleep. And while these painful headaches can affect our moods and our productivity, they can also seriously affect our memories. Not getting enough sleep in and of itself can impair your memory, but that, in conjunction with frequent migraines, is enough to permanently damage your short-term memory retention. In the September 1998 edition of *American Health for Women*, Dr. Robin West, a psychologist at the University of Florida, Gainesville notes that being stressed strains the memory, but "add lack of sleep to the mix, and it's no wonder we're literally losing our minds." Being tired makes it hard to focus, which makes it difficult to get information into our short-term storage banks.

Also, our cumulative sleep debts have a serious impact on the monetary debt of American companies, who, according to the aforementioned *Houston Chronicle* article, lost $150 billion every year through the decreased productivity of their sleepy employees. People also spend money on sleep aids and caffeine pills.

Not surprisingly, people who carry high sleep debts are also more susceptible to disease and micro-sleep. Dr. Max Hirshkowitz, Director of Baylor, a sleep lab, explains in the May 27, 1998, *Sacramento Bee* that "micro-sleep" is the instantaneous dozing off which lasts less than a minute, but at 60 mph, five seconds is long enough. Micro-sleep is the attributed cause of such disasters as the Chernobyl explosion, the Exxon *Valdez* crash, and the twenty-five to fifty people killed every day in this country by those sleeping behind the wheel. That article goes on to exclaim, "that's like a 747 crashing every other week, with no survivors." Sadly, the National Highway Safety Administration reports that there will be a 20 percent increase in that number Sunday, the day we "spring ahead" into daylight savings time. So from headaches and memory loss to monetary costs and micro-sleep, sleep debts affect us all in some way.

Now that we understand why we need to be alarmed by letting our sleep balance plunge below zero, we can open our eyes to better examine the three causes of sleep debts. First, as Dr. Stanley Coren, a neuropsychologist at the University of British Columbia, explains in the August 2, 1998, edition of the *Boston Globe*, the "chronic lack of sleep experienced by the American population is a direct result of the industrial revolution." In the nineteenth century, the hours of the day were extended due to the widespread use of

electric lights and the elimination of the midday nap. Experts at the National Sleep Foundation say we need between eight and nine hours of sleep a night to function at our peak, and most of us are only getting seven or less.

Having too much to do is another cause of sleep deprivation. Daily chores, TV, the Internet, caffeine, and simple insomnia, which affects over 35 million Americans, are all demands on our sleep time, and with 24-hour Wal-Marts, 120 channels on cable, and the world at the tips of our keyboards, there's always something to do, so sleep loses out.

And with all this, Dr. Judith Leech, head of the Ottawa Hospital sleep lab, presents the third cause in the April 19, 1998, edition of the *Ottawa Citizen*. She says that in addition to how much we sleep, "how well we sleep" is important. A fitful night of tossing and turning, although it may last ten hours, does us about as much good as six hours of deep, sound, relaxing sleep. So, the industrial revolution, too much to do, and poor sleep quality all influence our insufficient sleeping habits.

Now that we understand both the causes and the effects of sleep debts, we can cozy up to some solutions on both the societal and personal levels. Dr. Richard Costriotta, director of the University of Texas-Houston sleep lab, exclaims: "Welcome to the 90's" where more than half of us are sleep deprived and there's nothing we can do about it. Well, that's not quite true.

To completely eliminate this plague in our society, I propose that we undo the industrial revolution, destroy all the light bulbs, and revert to an agrarian society. Okay, so that's not really plausible, but there are steps we can take to eliminate our sleep deprivation without diminishing the last two centuries of progress.

First, we need to recognize the limitations of societal solutions. While some may say that big businesses will never be sensitive to the needs of their employees, an article in the March 28, 1999, *Times-Picayune* tells about several companies in the New Orleans area that have implemented nap time as part of the daily work routine. This drastically diminishes the sleep debts of their employees and increases productivity and benefits to the company.

If you're not lucky enough to work for one of these companies, don't worry, because most of the solutions lie on the personal level. In his 1999 book, *Power Sleep*, Dr. James Maas lists several tips for putting your sleep balance back in the black.

- First and foremost, make an appointment with sleep and don't be late.
- Secondly, turn the bedroom into a conducive sleeping environment; eliminate distractions such as the TV, computers, and work out equipment; make it quiet and dark, and lower the temperature so it's a few degrees cooler than the rest of the house.
- Next, establish a routine before bed; take a warm shower, eat a light snack with warm milk, unwind, and allow yourself twenty minutes to fall asleep.
- Finally, he advises to avoid evening exercise and caffeine and nicotine, if not altogether, at least within four hours of bedtime, because these activities lead to increased heart rate, which makes it difficult to relax.

By following these simple steps, we can eliminate our sleep debts and be happier, healthier, more productive individuals.

Today we've taken a look at our National Debt. Our national sleep debt, that is. First we woke up to some of its alarming effects, then we opened our eyes to better understand its causes, and finally we cozied up to some simple steps that both businesses and all of us can take.

Unlike so many other plagues that haunt our society today, we know both what causes and what cures sleep deprivation, so the real tragedy here is that two-thirds of us are still suffering unnecessarily.

So, before National Sleep Awareness Week and this tournament are over, take the time to pay off your sleep debt before your body declares biological bankruptcy. Sleep tight and don't let your sleep debt bite.